COLOR
PLANNING

for Business and Industry

ALSO BY HOWARD KETCHAM

Paint It Yourself

*How to Use Color and Decorating
Designs in the Home*

Color: Its Theory and Application

COLOR
PLANNING

for Business and Industry

BY HOWARD KETCHAM

President, Howard Ketcham, Inc., Color, Design and Illumination Engineering

HARPER & BROTHERS, PUBLISHERS, NEW YORK

For
Mary Louise

CONTENTS

Contents

Contents

ix

Contents

FOREWORD

I first met Howard Ketcham in 1936. He had just announced and demonstrated the "colorcable"—a method of transmitting color from anywhere to anywhere in a matter of minutes. As one of the editors of *Time*, I thought this quite fascinating invention deserved national attention and I wrote a two-column story for the magazine about Ketcham's then just-beginning experiments with color. As it turned out, they were the dawn of a dazzling day for American industry.

Strangely enough, most businesses paid little attention to the color of things back in 1936. I say strangely because the emotional aspect of color is as timeless as sunsets. Primitive men painted their bodies to frighten enemies; primitive *and* modern women do the same with other ends in view. The Empress Josephine, at odds with her sister-in-law, the Duchess of Guastalla, had the ballroom for a state reception painted blue purposely to clash with the Duchess' green dress; when the Blackfriars Bridge in London was repainted from black to green, the number of suicide jumps decreased 33 per cent; Knute Rockne kept his Notre Dame gridmen keyed up during the half in a red dressing room, while the visiting team was lulled with a soporific blue. Yet only recently has American business realized the potent value of color selection in product design and worker's morale. Howard Ketcham pioneered this significant development.

Proceeding on the theory that constructive color planning makes dollars-and-cents sense for nearly every branch of business and industry, Ketcham demonstrated that color has more than an aesthetic value. Used with skill, it has an emotional impact that can enhance the utility as well as the appeal of innumerable products. And it can pay realistic dividends in greater employee safety and general well-being. The old idea that color selection for products, plants and offices was a matter of personal preference and taste seems to be giving way gradually to reliance on professional color engineering. Today many of the country's most important concerns—e.g., Pan American World Airways, Chrysler, Standard-Vacuum Oil Company, Goodrich, Du Pont —take advantage of Howard Ketcham's color-full advice.

And he can point to practical results over the years: 19,000 Cities Service Oil Company gas stations, for example, increased their premium fuel sales over 50 per cent after the stations were changed to green and white from their former, more somber, black and white; color planning for United States Steel Homes helped jump their sales by 40 per cent; and over five hundred products—from fountain pens to vacuum cleaners—have benefited from Ketcham's diversified experience.

Now comes this practical and provocative book. Thirty years' work with color is behind it, and the contents lead almost literally to the pot of gold at the end of the rainbow. Since I first wrote about Howard Ketcham twenty-two years ago, color engineering has come of age. He deserves a big part of the credit as its instigator. I am glad once again to commend his work to your attention.

JAMES PARTON

February, 1958   Publisher, *American Heritage*

PREFACE

Have you ever considered how much color contributes to your life, your job, your appearance, your home, your product, every day, everywhere? Do you realize how much color is involved in your work, in everyday business? Every day at your desk, drawing board, factory, store, office, with your fellow workers, executives, vendors, customers, friends, visitors—all of these involve thousands of color decisions every year of your life.

Effective use of color can contribute to your prospects of success in your social life and in business if all your color choices and arrangements are consciously directed along practical lines.

Creative color engineering is the ability and art of increasing the impulse appeal of a product. It is the intangible ingredient which, when well engineered, creates visual value and lasting satisfaction with the merchandise, product or environment.

This book is based on three decades of practical work with color; first as an art director for the H. K. McCann Advertising Agency (the forerunner of McCann-Erickson), then as a Director of the Color Advisory Service of the Fabrics and Finishes

Division of E. I. du Pont de Nemours and Company, Incorporated, and since 1935, as the pioneer in introducing professional color planning to American business. In this book, liberal use is made of our organization's wide experience with all segments of industry—from small businesses to the country's largest corporations. In all our color work we have been able to combine firsthand knowledge with experience and to make a firsthand study of the color-buying actions and reactions of people. We have verified many of their color likes and dislikes, attitudes, wants, and desires. Combining all this information, I have incorporated the parts applicable to business and industry in this book. You will find a wealth of actual case histories detailed, setting forth proven methods of creating more sales and consumer satisfaction. This is not a book on color theory, it is based on practical color work. I have been in touch with thousands of businessmen through market surveys, writings, talks, and personal interviews. Through color engineering, I have helped the sale of both tangibles and intangibles by every conceivable color-planning method.

As profit margins decline on older products, manufacturers in nearly all industries are placing more and more reliance on new product colors to bolster sales and earnings. When business expands and becomes more competitive, a more skillful and effective use of color becomes absolutely essential. So here is a timely book.

In the following pages you will find messages applicable to one or more of your own business problems, related to color. When you have read this book, you will have a workable idea of what color engineering means or can mean to your business. You will see how others employ colors to get results and you will learn how the right use of color can help you sell more of anything produced and used in the modern world.

HOWARD KETCHAM

March 28, 1958
New York City

HOW COLOR SELLS

You've got to be color-blind or indifferent to a mirror to over-look Mr. Natale Costa's newsstand at a busy New York street corner. So pointed out the New York *World Telegram and Sun* recently.

Nat Costa, who is sixty-three, has proved some theories on the psychology of salesmanship. He painted his newsstand a canary yellow, posted the mirror at a strategic position, and saw sales jump 100 per cent.

"Yellow's the best for a customer," he explained. "It wakes 'em up, just like the sun in the morning. Some's in a hurry to get home. When they get here they got to open their eyes. And then they remember to buy a paper."

He says he'll never go back to the traditional drab green stand.

"You see anything yellow, you look at it right away. You see anything green, you don't bother. It's too dead. See that cab over there? It's yellow. You look at it right away."

He carries out his startling color scheme even to the electric light bulbs and paperweights that hold down his papers.

He tells why he gives the public an attractive place to trade:

1

"Looks then like you got respect for people. It's just like a person don't want to walk in mud."

Mr. Costa has learned a lesson which is coming home to many American businesses: color has become one of today's powerful aids in merchandising and sales, in practically every phase of American business and industry. Functional color planning is now increasing sales of all kinds of consumer goods, from fountain pens to prefabricated houses. Functional color planning is building new profits in retail operations ranging from supermarkets to shoe stores.

So significant is the correct use and application of color today that it supplies an excellent earmark for the progressive, modern company. It often reveals whether a company is well managed, well acquainted with the problems of modern merchandising, and well equipped to face competition.

Yes, color sells goods—and attracts customers. The New York Telephone Company learned this from one of its junior executives in a simple but effective experiment. Returning from duty with the Marine Corps in the Pacific, he noticed that the telephone booths at Grand Central Station in New York City were painted olive drab—a shade that he associated with camouflage and concealment. Reasoning that the phone company doesn't want to hide its booths, he suggested that some of those in Grand Central should be painted a bright, eye-catching red. The result? During the two-week period of the test, the number of calls made from the red booths increased 600 per cent.

COLOR SELLS TELEPHONES

The telephone company also finds that color sells in the home. Colored handsets—in eight colors that I am proud to have created—are supplanting black telephones as fast as orders can be filled. Their colors blend perfectly with both traditional and contemporary room and office decorating. In addition to aiding a vivid accent note to any interior, they make telephoning more efficient because they are so easy to see, more pleasant because

2

they so easily adapt to the accent color requirments of any type of décor. They are more fun to use, easier to advertise and merchandise. Since they became available to telephone subscribers in 1955, the colored handsets have turned into an asset for business, too. They have been used to create individuality and prestige in showrooms, display rooms, and offices. Millions of the phones are now in use.

COLOR SELLS TO THE MASS MARKET

In retailing, color has exerted a tremendous influence. It has long been easy for people with lots of money to find matching or blending home-furnishing colors in the smart stores. Now large organizations, dedicated to the mass market, are willing and eager to give the same advantages in color co-ordination to the small-home owner with his limited budget. Look at Sears, Roebuck. Not long ago Sears inaugurated a program featuring sixteen basic colors in what it calls its "Harmony House" line. Each color has a descriptive name for easy identification. Each is available in a complete line of home furnishings—rugs, venetian blinds, draperies, shower curtains, bathroom fixtures, toilet paper, bedspreads, lampshades, wallpaper, paint, dishes—anything.

Sears gets many of its four-color "Harmony House" advertisements back with an open-ticket request from housewives to supply every item in the illustration. Obviously, this is a great service to customers, particularly those remote from shopping centers. But its big significance is the recognition that color co-ordination is now part of the thinking that the majority of American women—in all income groups—apply to their home surroundings.

COLOR SELLS CARS

The proof lies right outside on the street. As the seller's market in cars tapered off after World War II, the growing competition among automobile manufacturers put an un-

3

precedented rainbow of color out on the road. Two-tone cars became commonplace; three-tone cars appeared out of the spray booths. From dealers all over the country came the plea for more colors, better colors, colors that would sell.

The leading auto companies have reacted, sensibly enough, by making their color-concerned styling directors vice-presidents; by establishing huge, well-equipped, and separate color and styling departments; by erecting giant research centers tailored, among other things, to the job of developing new and better colors and color combinations in fabrics, finishes, and plastics, and to the job of getting them out into the showrooms.

COLOR BRINGS IN THE PASSENGERS

Progressive railroads like the New York Central, the Southern, the Long Island, the Western Pacific, and the Santa Fe know this. They use color effectively. Color has made their train interiors easier and less costly to maintain and more pleasant to travel in. They have employed exterior color for advertising identification, for glamour and distinction, for better visibility, and for a more cheerful and attractive appearance. In every case they are finding double dividends: more passengers and happier passengers (the second a most important consideration when a rate rise is in the offing).

COLOR SELLS HOUSES

The executive editor of a leading builder's magazine estimates that we will need 1,500,000 to 2,000,000 new dwelling units a year by the 1960's, units that a newly married couple can afford. With the diminishing supply of lumber and the cost of painting and repainting a house, many of these units will be surfaced with metal, plastics, or ceramics, colored through various methods. Modern builders agree that the trend in homes is toward distinctive and colorful appearance and modern conveniences, rather than toward size. This trend will be especially strong as we build mass housing to meet that demand. Color will help builders avoid the slumlike housing of the past decade. However these new houses are made, color will be *the* important factor in their sale.

COLOR SELLS FIXTURES

The Briggs Manufacturing Company is a leading maker of colorful bathroom fixtures. Since it brought out its new color line it is finding, like so many other firms, that color means beauty and beauty makes sales.

Briggs has evolved a dynamic plan to present its color line to its customers. Realizing that many people have trouble envisioning colored fixtures from small samples, swatches, or porcelain chips, Briggs hired me to evolve a series of bathroom color ensembles, complete with advertising and display-room ideas and recommendations. It then prepared a handsome four-color brochure showing how the company's products could be featured in color-planned model bathrooms.

Briggs is using this integrated bathroom color styling in its ads and in display brochures for builders, plumbers, and architects; and Briggs Beautyware colors are finding greatly increased acceptance. Briggs has found that color can be a powerful sales tool indeed. Women want bathrooms just like the ones pictured in the advertisements. To get them, many a woman will re-do her entire bathroom and this procedure sets up an ideal impetus toward the sale of tub, basin, and toilet fixture featured in the ads.

COLOR SELLS APPLIANCES

John R. McCord, Director of Public Relations for the Ferro Corporation, recently told a group of appliance makers to " . . . face up to one basic fact. Color has become the greatest . . . technique for creating obsolescence in appliances as well as other goods.

"Color percentages in this field have tripled or quadrupled

in a few short years. That is to say from a start of less than 5 per cent in 1952–53, the present percentage is running anywhere from 10 per cent to as high as 30 per cent as reported by some manufacturers on some items.

"General Electric indicates 25 per cent colored appliances in the first quarter of 1958, as against 11.2 per cent during the whole of 1955. Some products in their lines are up to 30 per cent in color.

"Our Ferro porcelain enamel figures show we doubled our color activity in 1956 against the first quarter of 1955."

Quite a showing in this great and growing business.

COLOR SELLS BY MAIL

Consider a letter. A colorful envelope and letterhead paper are more intriguing to the recipient than the conventional white stationery. Color gives your direct mail more selling punch. Experience, following my suggestion, convinced the circulation staff of *Life* Magazine on this point. *Life* has used appropriately colored envelopes and paper for letters and subscription prospects ever since.

COLOR SELLS IN MANY MORE WAYS

Color contributes to sales appeal in myriad other areas. Let's examine four more of them—dentistry, funeral homes, fountain pens, and gasoline service stations.

Nowhere is the right color more important than it is to the wearer of false teeth. The user benefit imparted by correct tooth color is incalculable. The better their color—the more natural the teeth look—the more word-of-mouth advertising, so to speak, they're going to get. Here, color helps build good will and confidence in the dentist! Luxene, Inc., a leading false-tooth manufacturer, has boosted sales with only twelve carefully engineered colors in its product line.

In his contacts with the public the funeral director has much

6

the same job of co-ordinating public presentations as an executive of a large industrial organization. The alert, progressive director, therefore, carefully considers the over-all appearance of each physical thing that the public can identify with his business. A good color plan for the chapel, display room, and visitation rooms can be his most profitable and least costly stock-in-trade. The colors for each of these areas, while purposely keyed low in soft, quiet nuances, can give each room from parlor to chapel a desirable degree of cheer.

One of our funeral-home clients, W. L. Bustard, leading funeral director of Casper, Wyoming, has proved the worth of well-planned color in his business. "Color engineering is doing a job for us," he wrote in a letter to a fellow funeral director. "We know that there is a definite decrease in the number of families that break down because of emotional crisis—the attractive surroundings help sustain emotional stability when people are most likely to be at the breaking point. We have already shown an increase in percentage of available services, which we did not expect for another year."

It was more than thirty years ago that colored fountain pens went on the market. Up to that time fountain pens were made of black rubber. The man responsible for the idea that colored plastic pens would sell was a jeweler named Sheaffer. He was proved right by the fact that the industry's sales shot up astronomically. Today you rarely see anyone write with a black fountain pen.

A psychologically correct color plan for the Cities Service Oil Company increased premium fuel sales over 50 per cent. In 1957, campaigns introducing high-octane fuels stressed fuel-pump colors for customer identification and company prestige. In this same year, Cities Service began selling three grades of gas from pumps specially planned for visibility and sales appeal. This color planning was mine.

This has been a kaleidoscopic survey of color in action as a sales tool. It is a success story, and its success has depended on the understanding of big business executives and Mr. Costa alike. This book is designed to give *you* a chance to share in that understanding, to watch color in action and to find out why color works as it does. It will talk, among other things, about color's effect on sales, on safety, on office morale, and on national defense. It will examine color on the job in planes, buses, markets, stores, advertising, TV, clothing, beauty aids, and a host of other fields. It will elaborate on the examples we've just touched on and it will give you more examples galore.

What then can color do for *your* business?

COLOR COMMENTS

In a recent Army-Navy football game the Navy coach switched the colors on the players' shirts to pale gold letters on a baby blue background. Confusion hit the Press Box as no one, including the announcer calling the plays, could distinguish the numbers on any of the Navy players. Proper contrast would have ensured legibility. Dark blue on light blue would have done the job.

Substitution of aluminum paint for black on bedsprings boosted one manufacturer's sales by 25 per cent.

The introduction of tangerine-colored cotton bags in the citrus trade increased the demand for bags from 1,250,000 to more than 10,000,000 in one season.

Correct colors for U.S. Steel's prefabricated homes helped jump sales 40 per cent in 1955.

A yacht incorporating the author's color and design ideas became the Century Boat Company's best seller and, at the time of this writing, is oversold for the next three years.

Returns of piece goods fell off 60 per cent in Gimbel's Philadelphia store with the introduction of color-corrected lighting.

THE USES OF COLOR THROUGH THE AGES

There is no element in our experience which yields us more immediate or more varied pleasure than color. And few things in life are more appreciated, more important, and less understood than color. To understand color, though, we can helpfully look to the past. Behind today's trend to more color extends an ageless background of tradition, education, observation, training, and experience. Scores of color associations are indelibly stamped on the pattern of our racial subconscious.

THE ORIGINS OF COLOR

What were the original colors? Where did they come from? And how were they used?

We do not know.

Darwin, in his *Origin of Species*, theorizes that once, before animal life evolved on our planet, green was the sole color of all vegetation. This green was chlorophyll, still present in nature. Out of changes and variation in plant chemistry, new colors were evolved. When insects appeared they were attracted by the brighter-colored plants, thus helping to fertilize and propagate them. In this way, flowering plants may illustrate the first usefulness of color in gaining favorable attention. Today, the plants that need insect help for fertilization are the brightly colored ones; those that depend on the wind are more drab.

COLORS DEVELOP

From the beginning, man has always tried to utilize the colors provided by nature in embellishing his arts and crafts. The man of the Stone Age depicted in color what he saw about him—animals, vegetation, the rainbow, fire, sunset, sunrise. His first colors would have been vegetable and animal extracts or natural earth pigments. He seems to have traditionalized certain reactions to specific colors, relating yellow and red and blue to sunlight and fire and sky or water, respectively. These primary pigments seem to have expressed for him the cycles of life—at its morning, in full vigor, and at the ebb. So yellow means to us exultation or wisdom; red, vigor and passion; blue, peace and idealism.

Primitive cave dwellings were ornamented with charcoal (usually burnt bone), red from hematite (iron oxide), yellow ochers (limonite or other ores or metallic clays), and white lime. Earth colors were applied as flat washes or as dots. Whether or not Paleolithic man's artistic aptitude influenced the early art of ancient Egypt and Babylonia, there are rough parallels between decorated artifacts found in prehistoric Egyptian tombs, for example, and primitive European cave drawings. Colors of primary intensity were used by primitive man because he knew little of the art of mixing colors to produce subdued effects. He enjoyed his colors as he found them in the form of pebbles, shells, ocherous earths, feathers, and flowers.

In time, the ability of early races to depict and decorate outgrew their limited palettes. Brighter and more varied colors were sought as civilization advanced. Man's ingenuity raced

10

with his color craving. A blue color was obtained from a substance now recognized as a product of plant decomposition. The Egyptians secured alizarin from the madder plant, *Rubia tinctorum*. Scarlet was produced from the kermes insects, and our color-name vermilion is derived from *vermiculus,* the Latin word for the "little worm" that supplied the dye. Some pigments were obtained from the red oxides of iron and other ores. Ultramarine was made from lapis lazuli. The Phoenicians obtained Tyrian purple from the mollusks Purpura and Murex; it is a hueless secretion that becomes colorful when exposed to light or heat.

Descriptions of color up to modern times—in the Bible, for instance—abound with familiar terms: "and there was a rainbow about the Throne like an emerald to look upon." (Rev. 4:3) The color language of antiquity is characterized by a scarcity of names, and consequently the literature of the past contains little of a nature to give us any specific impression of color usage. An instance is the Sanskrit word for "blood," *rudhira.* But blood is not a stable red. In the veins, it appears purple. Arterial blood is a vivid crimson; in stains, blood is brown, and it dries black. The language of color suffered from such poverty for many thousands of years.

EGYPT: "COLOR ENGINEERING"

The Egyptians made outstanding use of color in symbols, hieroglyphics, and in pictorial representations of their life, and they employed many basic colors. They had a green derived, in powder form, from the brilliant mineral malachite, and from green earth; they had a yellow secured from a soft, bright mineral, orpiment; they had a blue from cobalt. In their fresco work, they used black outlines derived from vegetable or bone carbons. Their medium of egg whites and vinegar for such colors was later employed by the Greeks.

They roamed far afield for their color supplies, obtaining bright orange-yellow from Syrian orpiment, other yellows from

11

saffron—derived from the yellow crocus. Red sandarac they brought from deposits of arsenic sulphide near the Red Sea. Indigo was made from an Asiatic plant, and green from a mixture of native coppery blue with the henna plant.

The glaring sun of the bright Egyptian Nile Valley first gave rise to the principles of color engineering, adding functional use to the aesthetic appeal of color. In the Nile regions, thanks to the absence of rain which helped preserve the brilliance of original colors, we have evidence dating back nearly six thousand years to show that the Egyptians were even then using light-reflection values of colors to obtain some practical effects. Due to the blinding glare of the Egyptian sun, homes were constructed practically without windows. This enabled the Egyptians to rest their eyes while indoors. Not wishing to dwell in dull gloom, they saw to it that their walls were both decorative and practical. Because strong, bright colors reflect light best, modern Egyptians maintain the use of such colors in their homes. To this day, vivid ceiling hues, cool-colored walls, and glowing rugs turn heavy shadows into rich bloom. Much of the efficiency of our present-day use of color in dark apartments and closely packed city homes is successful because it applies lessons learned in the distant past.

Other Egyptian uses of color were equally effective. The Egyptians decorated their homes in color within and without. Their pottery and mummy cases were equally colorful, and Sir Humphrey Davy declared more than a century ago that "Egypt practiced calico printing in a manner similar to the moderns." They seldom used pure hues but employed reduced shades or tones—greens ranging from the brightness of emerald to grayed dark olive, yellows in warm tones, reds scaled toward brown, and low-value blues.

For sheer originality, the Egyptians were hard to surpass in the art of coloration. Yet the color conventions of the ancients were based upon casual observation of nature's colorings combined with a primitive sense of decorative value in the use of available pigments. As a consequence, with the pigments so

12

impure and so limited, results were far from realistic. The Egyptians knew the color of skin was not yellow, but yellow ocher was the one pigment closest to an olive skin, and evidently this convention satisfied them.

NEW COLOR IDEAS IN OLD GREECE

The early Aegeans showed the same progressive attitude in dealing with color that later marked the Hellenic culture. In Crete, well before the growth of the mainland culture, a feeling of movement through provocative color applications was introduced. In the frescoes of the palace of Knossos appear colors unfettered by naturalism: blue-green monkeys, blue-spotted hounds, a rose-colored boar, and a pink horse disport themselves. This mode of coloration appears much later in the seventeenth-century art of India, where tempera illuminations portrayed the "essence of the subject" with pink elephants, violet horses, and blue divinities.

Realism, harmony, balance, and rhythm were developed in Greek color application. Never were adjoining areas on an architectural structure or on an animate figure allowed to be in the same color. For example, a blue Doric cornice would require use of another color on the adjoining guttae. In this particular period of civilization, consideration of balance and rhythm in color distribution was introduced.

The Greeks used vivid colors on their temples and in their homes. They used color to decorate walls and wood panels and vases. But color was always subordinated to form, and light and shade were always considered more important than hue. The Greeks introduced brilliant reds and blues on the exteriors of their buildings and subtle muted hues were featured on the interiors. The conventional Greek palette featured tints of red-orange, blue-green, yellow-orange, creamy white, deep blue, red-violet, and yellow-green.

13

ROME'S CONTRIBUTION
TO THE ART OF COLOR

To Greece we owe the idea of utility subordinated to pure beauty. And the Greeks promoted realism in the use of color. But the Romans promoted the idea of order and efficiency in the use and application of color. The Romans were the first to use stencils for painting colored borders, and they were the first to paint stone or plaster to imitate marble and granite. As far as color is concerned, they preserved and codified the cultural attainments of two earlier periods.

Much of what we know about Roman color usage is gained from the ruins of Pompeii and Herculaneum, rediscovered in the eighteenth century. Luckily the original appearance of these colors was preserved through the centuries by a protective cover of ashes. Samples of ocher, massicot, arsenic, vermilion, red lead, cochineal, blue cobalt glass, copper green, and brown umber were all discovered in the Baths of Titus in Pompeii. A study of the wall colors in other Pompeian ruins shows a naturalistic color technique. Black backgrounds were employed to offset the brilliant sunlight of southern Italy. Intricate designs were employed on a variety of background color tints. Other color schemes featured white landscapes on black backgrounds. The Romans also introduced here the principles of advancing and retreating color, to establish a series of planes on a flat surface.

It is interesting to note that the Romans had their commercial problems in producing color. One emperor complained of the cost of the purple dye from Tyre, a price-control law covered the import of cinnabar for red pigment from Spain, and the historian Pliny wrote that one firm had adulterated a large color batch with local clay.

From Britain comes even more evidence about Roman colors. Scattered fragments in the ruins of Roman-British architecture reveal a confident use of interior colors, more restrained than in primitive or peasant art and suited to the British climate.

14

In some instances the Roman designers divided wall spaces with strips of plain color; on other walls, where marginal borders were of considerable width, the borders comprised many bands or lines of color. The dado of a room might be a plain band of color or a horizontal bar running into margins. One Roman dado had a row of alternating round and square panels, set with leaves and ears of grain, on a red background between dark upper and lower bands.

Red was the dominant color in many of the old Roman homes in Britain. One home had a combination of red and white with black stripes, blue, a grayed blue with red and yellow, and a combination of red, yellow, and white. Rooms with red backgrounds had walls divided into panels by margins in varied colors, with insets of floral designs, birds, human figures, nymphs, stars, and the like. In still another home, white, dark blue, and purple were marginal borders for red walls, with a yellow trellis pattern superimposed on the border and various devices inset in the trellis. Pale blue and yellow bordered another red background over a blue-gray dado; on the yellow margin were designs in red interlacing with conventional foliage in green.

Observers have commented that these treatments showed commanding abilities in associating a variety of hues. The restrained colors gained from the brightest day, yet had warmth and vitality to enliven the dull weather which beset Britain then as now. Patches of brightness embellished the color scheme, and the cheering shades of floral design gave the whole the freshness of life.

FROM THE COLORFUL ORIENT

While the Western world was experiencing a rebirth of sharp, bright colors, Asia and the Middle East were creating delicate hues that are the subject of wondering comment to this day.

Ancient China created the famous Chinese red lacquer of

15

ground cinnabar, duplicating it finally by artificial means. Lampblack, obtained from the soot of resin burned in a sealed chamber, was made there dozens of centuries ago. The embroideries of the Memorial of Rights, in 2205 B.C., established combinations of five colors (blue, red, yellow, white, and black) as a standard in Chinese painting. And early Chinese painters even used outlines to separate and to blend colors, with appropriate outline colors to fit each requirement. The Orient was and is a land of sophistication in color.

The Sung period, tenth to thirteenth centuries A.D., produced the profusion of delicately colored porcelains which exemplify the all-time peak of color art. Chinese ware dating back to that period offers bluish-green grays whose delicacy is almost transparent. Sung porcelain presented fine buff interpretations of biscuit colors and creamy whites whose excellence is imitated to this day. Apple green was the best-loved color. A darker and bluer green called "cucumber," a brilliant emerald green, and the royal family's yellow—the "color of dried bones"—all these are still much admired. Tang yellows (from the seventh to the tenth centuries) were browner, and a range of pinks appeared in the Ming specimens (fourteenth through seventeenth centuries).

For modern wall and woodwork decorations, oriental tints are particularly favored. For these, the delicate colorings of the early Ming and Sung porcelain are excellent inspirations. The dainty transparent quality of their bluish-green grays, their exquisite pale and gray blues, their pale translucent greens, and the light gray-green and opaque blue-green—developments of Lung-Chan—are unexcelled. Certainly few modern color adaptations can compare with the remarkable buffs, creams, and biscuit colors of the early Sung porcelain.

Another high point of color development was reached in the East centuries later—this time in Persia. Here, in the sixteenth and seventeenth centuries, carpets, embroideries, pottery, and frescoes became famous for their colors. In fact, a special powder blue of that period is still considered remarkable.

The Persians are recognized as among the greatest decorative colorists of all time, because of the rich beauty of their color selections and the rare skill with which these colors were combined and applied. The most notable color prepared by the Persians, a favorite with them, is a soft, grayed turquoise, similar to the color in certain Ming creations. Its subtle gray undertone lends itself admirably to a wide range of secondary color accents. Green was another hue much favored in oriental art, particularly lemon greens.

Powder blue was first used in the East, chiefly as a background for gold ornamentation. Mazarine, a blue similar to Nanking, was also used as a foil for design accents. Mohammedan blue was another popular color among the orientals.

Cotton blue, Turkey red, Bokhara blue, and Bokhara red were introduced in rugs of Turkey, India, and Persia. These colors are highly prized to this day for decorative purposes.

AMERICAN INDIAN COLORS

Halfway around the world, the highly civilized Mexicans and Peruvians as well as the primitive Apache and Pueblo tribes of Arizona and New Mexico were interesting and consistent users of color art. They made extensive use of red, yellow, brown, green, orange, purple, and solferino. Even in ancient times, and among primitive peoples, we see that color application—in one from or another—was truly a universal phenomenon.

MEDIEVAL COLORS

In the medieval period the use of color became even more widespread. The English peasantry, for example, painted handles, spokes, shafts, and other sections of their implements with greens and blues. The aristocracy used more colors than had ever been used before. They even painted wainscoting to imitate woven hangings and painted cloth to imitate early tapestry. The term "Dark Ages," in truth, then, is a misnomer. The light of color application never dimmed, although artificial restraints often limited its use, particularly among the humble. The Emperor Charlemagne, for example, prescribed conservative gray as the color for the common people, in keeping with his own taste for quiet dress.

Three great influences dominated medieval color applications: feudalism, the Church, and the rise of the guilds in the cities. Let's look at these three influences.

FEUDALISM: FORMAL COLOR

With feudal social organization came the meaningful ornamentation of heraldry, based on a limited group of symbolical figures and a small number of colors. The heraldic colors were red, blue, black, green, purple, gold, and silver, variously combined. With the rise of the European silk industry, the nobility began to clothe itself in the colors of its coats of arms, with the heraldic symbols painted or embroidered thereon. Soon everyone connected with the noble family, down to the lowest menial, wore the family colors. Then the particolored dress developed, with the wearer clad from head to foot in two or four vertical lines of heraldic color. Eventually, as the city bourgeoisie infringed on the nobles' prerogatives in dress color, the upper circle retired in disdain to their castles, affected more restrained costume colors, and retained the heraldic colors as a livery or uniform for their servants.

COLOR AND THE CHURCH

The Church employed a wealth of color in its structures, ceremonies, and vestments. Specified colors were used to represent virtues, vices, and emotions; the illiterate peasant was able to understand from the use of those colors the feelings that were supposed to follow. Hues, values, and chromas of the various colors changed through the centuries.

BLACK is the traditional color of mourning. It is the liturgical color for Good Friday.

18

GREEN is the color of the Epiphany season in the Church. It marks the visitation of the Magi and the initiation into the life of Christ.

PURPLE is the color of Advent and Lent. Used in anticipation of Christmas and Easter. This is the color of sorrow.

RED is the color of Pentecost. It commemorates the coming of the Holy Ghost.

WHITE is the color of purity. It symbolizes Christmas, Easter, and the Ascension.

Colors used by the Church in each country were selected in part according to local ideas of fitness. The adoption of color variations, and the symbolical meanings acquired through traditional use, were made possible when the growing supply of fabric materials permitted the churches to maintain vestments beyond the minimum needs of daily, Sunday, and festival use. Then different colors were appropriated for the various festivals and for different classes of saints.

In England, colors were established for almost every day in the year. This scheme of color usage was maintained all over England and Scotland. The colors of altar hangings, bookmarks, and stoles were changed along with the vestments. The chief liturgical colors were red, white, green, yellow, blue, purple, and black; less often violet, tawny, orange-and-brown, dun, and "horseflesh color."

Another powerful impact of the Church on color came with the introduction of stained-glass windows in cathedrals; stained glass brought the emotional impact of color to its highest peak. The flowering of the glassmaker's talent came in the twelfth and thirteenth centuries with such masterpieces as the world-famous blue tree-of-Jesse window at Chartres Cathedral, a window which inspires complete submission to the mood of religious worship. This particular window is the best colored glass made and represents the most splendid color decoration the world has ever seen. No other material can compare in beauty of color with translucent glass. Even the Ravenna mosaics and Chinese porcelains are darkness beside this lancet in blue, red, green, yellow, and brown.

The finest medieval colored glass contained about twelve ingredients and was of irregular thickness, ranging from a quarter to a sixteenth of an inch. This thickness, caused by application of layer upon layer of color to obtain the right effect, helped build the effect by blending the background colors of most of the windows. The meticulous craftsmen created great variety in their color themes with the very few colors available to them. Rosy reds were used for flesh tints, and draperies achieved the tones of Tokay grapes. Juggling his available color elements, the glassmaker sometimes introduced a little of the complementary color to soften the tone of a red or blue. Yellow, for example, might be seen through a delicate purple haze, producing a soft banana-like tint.

COLOR AND THE NEW CITIES

As the feudal period gave way to an era of cities and city-states, clothing colors reflected the rising status of the bourgeoisie and the artisans.

Under the influence of the Crusades, the rich peasantry of south Germany and the city merchants of the western lands could strut in green hose and orange or purple doublet. Towns adopted color symbols, and a fourteenth-century procession in Paris saw aldermen, sheriffs, and guild-masters clad in outfits red on one side and white on the other. Trade guilds, too, adopted their own standards.

Color symbolism in the livery of servants of the nobility became even more widespread than formerly. Troubadours evolved a code in which different colors stood for moral or spiritual qualities, and lovers affected identical colors in their dress.

The Italian commoners, while affecting rich and gorgeous colors in the thirteenth and fourteenth centuries, were restrained by ancient tradition from the crudities in color seen in the dress of northern Europe. But by the fifteenth century all Europe went color-wild. Even well-to-do peasants came out in

20

shimmering garb, and strutting nobility in velvet and brocade reveled in multicolored play on various shades of color. A well-dressed woman might wear a high-crowned bonnet with brilliant veiling, green or blue skirts caught up by scarlet girdle to show the tapering points of red or blue shoes, hair dyed auburn, and a profusion of gems and cosmetics.

THE TAPESTRY COLORS OF FRANCE

Another burgeoning use of color came with the appearance of French tapestries: Gobelin tapestries have been recognized throughout the world for their color excellence since the beginning of the seventeenth century. The richness of their colorings, the understanding and skill that have directed the blending of these colors, the effetcive protection that has safeguarded the exclusive features pertaining to the manufacture of their special dye colors—all these have contributed to their lasting fame.

According to legend, the Gobelins once found themselves mysteriously unable to produce their famed rich red dye. Suddenly, no one knew why, their colors had become far inferior to the age-old standards. In France, this development had the effect of a national calamity. A government committee was appointed to serve under the director of the dye works of the Gobelins in an effort to help restore this lost art. Private funds, in addition to the government subsidy, were made available to help in the task. After a careful search along both banks of the river Seine on which the dye factory was located, a point of variation was disclosed. It developed that a slaughterhouse which once stood close to the banks of this river had been moved back, away from the water's edge. When this structure was restored to its original location, the blood of cattle once more mingled with the waters that contributed so strongly to the color processes of the Gobelins. Then the beautiful rich purity of their famed red hue returned. This incident shows how important small circumstances can be in helping men to achieve success in the art of color.

21

COLORS FROM OTHER SOURCES

Three splendid colors in wide use today originated with the famous stoneware of Flanders. Doulton ware is the basis of inspiration for Stone-of-Flanders blue-gray, Stone-of-Flanders blue, and Stone-of-Flanders deep blue—three of the modern world's most celebrated colors.

Other modern colors come from the efforts of Catherine de Médicis (1519–1589), Queen of France; she brought artists and craftsmen from Italy to develop color schemes for the Tuileries in Paris (today, many of our creative colorists still visit Italy to be similarly inspired). Many world-famous hues—still perpetuated—originated in the Riccardi Palace in Florence, home of the Medicis. Medici Blue has been much used as a background or foil color for architectural ornamentation.

French porcelain gave birth to a host of modern colors; in 1768 the secret of manufacturing hard porcelain from clay deposits was discovered at Sèvres, just outside Paris. The rich beauty of the unique Sèvres blue, jonquil yellow, grass green, rose du Barry, and rose du Pompadour became, and still is, the envy of the world. Many have tried to buy the secret of this color art from Sèvres, but to no avail. To protect this trade secret, the French government, since the time of Louis XV, has subsidized and rigidly controlled the manufacture of Sèvres porcelain. To this day no one has been able to duplicate exactly the famous Sèvres cobalt blue, "the King's blue."

Green and yellows became popular in France and England. In about the middle of the eighteenth century, Georgian green and William and Mary green were adapted from the French. Georgian green was high fashion in England until a lighter and more delicate green developed by the Adam brothers, renowned Scottish architects and colorists, superseded it in popularity.

Empire green and yellow were created during the first French Empire period. These historic colors were used in decorating the rooms of state during both the first and second French

Empires. They became the colors of high fashion in those times and their exact appearance was fixed by law.

ITALIAN DELLA ROBBIA COLORS

Deserving special note are Luca della Robbia's color decorations used on gates of the sacristy of the Cathedral of Florence. They were so beautiful that Michelangelo acclaimed them worthy to be the gates of Heaven. Blue-green and red accented with particles of gold leaf were typical of the colors of the Italian Renaissance.

DUTCH COLORISTS

Still another source of color was the careful pottery work of the Dutch. The Dutch were adept at selecting favored oriental pieces to be copied and exploited by the potters of Delft. Their first work duplicated, for the most part, the oriental originals. The Dutch soon developed a unique character of their own, however, in the colors in which they specialized. Their blue became a standard highly prized by connoisseurs. The Low Countries achieved another color distinction in that they originated the printing-ink industry, which was the first to start using color on a large scale.

1856: THE FIRST SYNTHETIC COLOR

It was not until Victoria's reign—one hundred years ago—that man found freedom from dependence upon nature's bounty to satisfy his craving for color. In 1856 an English chemist, Sir William Henry Perkin, produced the first synthetic color—aniline purple—known as mauve. The earth and natural colors available before his time were all weak in color value. Color came of age with the advent of his synthetic (coal tar) color. Described as "pink trying to be purple," it may have symbolized both the inner life and the color taste of the "mauve decade."

Now, freed from the limitations of natural sources for color in finishes, dyes, and printing, man entered an era in which his application of color was limited only by his own taste and ingenuity.

THE BOOM GETS GOING

Today, experience plus the accumulated knowledge of centuries serve us as true guides in meeting each color requirement. Forty years ago, color was little used in manufacture. Rooms were painted in limited, plain colors, and black prevailed in most items of popular use—the automobile, the fountain pen, men's suits. Today, even caskets are given appropriate, subdued but varied colors. Bath towels, blankets, powder puffs, men's shirts, houses, bed sheets, bathroom fixtures, kitchen appliances, and store interiors have changed from white to color.

This concern with color got under way at the time of World War I, when surplus profits helped to finance color experimentation. The businessmen of that era began to realize that color enhanced the appreciation of their wares—an almost forgotten fact, but one not unknown to the seventeenth-century earthenware potters of Delft or to the makers of Flanders stoneware.

In the haste of business to climb aboard the band wagon of rapidly expanding sales made possible through the appeal and newness of the innovation of color, many practical aspects of color selection and application were carelessly overlooked. Color was treated as a temporary fad, to be applied without too much consideration of aesthetic values or of the taste of the individual buyers of those days.

The explosive expansion of the car industry helped end color's haphazard days. As early as 1902, the *Saturday Evening Post* devoted considerable research to the impact of that twentieth-century miracle of individual ownership—the private automobile. Accurately the *Post* predicted the dates when motor-vehicle builders would adopt national advertising policies (1909), installment selling (1920), and color styling (1927) as a means of enlarging sales acceptance for automobiles. By 1929 each auto maker had his exclusive staff of color engineers. Many of these color pioneers—among them Harley Earl, vice-president of General Motors, and George Walker, vice-president of Ford—have done much to convince top management of the nation's largest manufacturers that appearance is as important as performance in influencing market acceptance for their products. Through color and smart design styling, the automobile became a symbol of prestige. Herbert Hoover once asked Calvin Coolidge why there were so many more automobile owners than telephone subscribers. President Coolidge replied, "You can't show off in a telephone booth."

And so the color boom was on.

HOW YOU CAN BENEFIT FROM COLOR RESEARCH

Before we proceed further into color planning, let's find out how much you now know about color and color preferences. Here's a brief quiz to give you an idea of your own color sense.

WHAT'S YOUR COLOR QUOTIENT?

Answers are listed in the Appendix on page 263. Score 10 points for each correct answer—and count yourself colorwise if you score 40 or more out of a possible 120.

1. What is the favorite color of: (a) Men _____
   (b) Women _____

2. At approximately what age do boys and girls start showing a marked preference for these two colors? _____

3. What has no size, shape, weight, taste nor can be seen without illumination, yet influences the appearance of almost everything we see? _____

4. The unaided eye can detect how many colors? 13,000 _____ 15,000 _____ 50,000 _____ 100,000 _____ 10,000,000 _____

5. Whose eyes are more subject to color blindess? Men _____ Women _____

6. (a) Name a cool color _____
   (b) Name a warm color _____

26

7. (a) What is a distance color? _____
    (b) What is a near color? _____
8. Are the primary colors that cannot be made by mixing, the
    same for pigments as for colored lights? _____
    If not, what is the difference? _____
9. Which of these color combinations is best for legibility?
    Red on white __ Yellow on Black __ Black on Yellow __
10. What are the four ways of obtaining contrast with color:
    (a) _____
    (b) _____
    (c) _____
    (d) _____
11. Does the choice of product color have much to do with the
    amount of new consumer business a business firm is likely to
    get?
12. How much larger noting audience does a half-page, four-color
    advertisement have in comparison with a half-page, black-
    and-white space? 25%   50%   85%   100%

                                                YOUR SCORE

Personal preferences often are based on good hard-headed
experience. Sometimes, on the other hand, they are rooted in
prejudice. Those prejudice-born preferences can do considerable damage, and when they are color prejudices, they can help
put you out of business.

The ultimate judge of color is the consumer. Product color
has to meet the test of the marketplace, and if your colors don't
meet that test you will see the result and see it fast in your
sales graph. Although we may not like it, today's motto must be
"our consumer, right or wrong." A vice-president of one of the
largest automobile companies puts it this way: "Our job today
is designing, coloring, and building what our customer wants,
not what we want."

That vice-president's statement is translated into fact within
his own company. The styling head of the same company
doesn't like green. He has no basis for his dislike—it's simply a
healthy, free-wheeling, personal prejudice against the hue. But
that styling executive takes elaborate pains to keep his prejudice

27

from influencing his company's color plans. He also knows that the consumer, not the manufacturer, is the ultimate arbiter of color.

How do we find out what colors the consumer is going to buy? How do we decide what colors to put on the market? The answer is through that healthy, sprawling, and fast-growing child in the social sciences, the survey.

The first surveys to determine color preference were taken by me when I was directing Du Pont's color advisory service. The survey was conducted for the Chevrolet automobiles at a time when Ford was outselling that car. But as Chevrolet went ahead and revamped their car colors according to survey facts, the sales picture did a complete turnabout.

Unfortunately, many totally unqualified firms are busily conducting motivational research (MR in the jargon) on color today. In many cases, MR seems to mean "more red." Color is not that simple, nor is the human response to colors.

WHY SURVEY?

Consumer color preference, like the woman in the Gershwin song, is a sometime thing. If consumer color wants were fixed, the color engineer would soon be out of a job. But they're not.

Color preferences vary from year to year. Consider cars. Consumer car color choices depend on a host of intangibles: on economic conditions, on climate, on color wants in other fields, on the desire of the car owner to let the people next door know that he's bought a new car.

Color preferences vary from place to place. Time was when you couldn't sell a pair of red socks in Philadelphia. Blue window shades roll up the Baltimore market, while Boston dwellers prefer to pull their shades in green.

Color preferences vary from age group to age group. Infants, as soon as they can distinguish color, grab red over other colors. Ages three to four prefer yellow. From thirteen to fifteen sex commences to play a part in basic color preferences; girls start to show a marked preference for red, and boys go for blue. Youths eighteen to twenty-one prefer dark colors, yet do not wear them. They choose gayer-colored clothes to live up to others' expectations. People age fifty-five to eighty or older tend to choose dark colors only because they believe people expect them to be conservative and sedate. Their actual preference is the opposite, with gay pink the top favorite.

But temporary fashions, bolstered by merchandising promotions, often run successfully if briefly against these long-term tendencies.

Color preferences vary from economic level to economic level. Some years back I conducted a survey on women's dress color preferences. Women in the under-$4,500 income group showed a marked preference for a pure medium-value purplish red; women in the over-$6,000 group did not include this color in their *ten* most wanted colors.

Each of these variations is a booby trap for the manufacturer selling color. A wrong decision on the basis of misinformation or lack of information in any one of these areas can do effective damage to sales. How do we find out what the consumer—no matter who she is or where she is—wants? It's simple. We ask her. That's why we survey.

SURVEYS IN ACTION

Surveys are becoming a representative tool for finding out what consumers want. Some survey programs are extensive and expensive. One advertising agency, for example, during a recent six-month period

—got 60,627 replies to 113 questionnaires
—obtained more than 10,500 opinions on 31 products
—wrote 779 case histories dealing with survey results on various items of merchandise

The agency polled people's opinions on tastes, smells, color, and style preferences. Its aim: to get the consumer facts necessary to support sales and advertising decisions.

That's what the color engineer does, too, when he surveys people on their color preferences. Let's look at three of the surveys I've conducted over the past few years and see some of the results they obtained.

Toiletware

A manufacturer of plastic toiletware sets asked for a new fast-selling color for his line. A survey showed a heavy demand for lilac, a revolutionary color at that time and one the manufacturer had not even considered. The manufacturer introduced the new color; it sold out in record time.

Wallboard

For over twenty-five years Celotex interior wallboard found good acceptance as a dry-wall construction material for home building. I suggested to Celotex that its wallboard would sell even more effectively if made in colors people found compatible with the then current home-furnishing colors. Celotex authorized me to conduct a nation-wide survey to help me determine these colors; the survey's results put the finger on a certain shade of blue-green and a pink with a bluish undertone. The two new colors went into the Celotex line. Demand for them remains heavy.

Women's Clothes

A manufacturer of women's clothes desired more general information on what color women wanted. Three thousand women were interviewed on their color choices, which were eventually winnowed down from 152 colors to 36. These 36 colors supplied the basis for much of the color planning for that manufacturer's fall line. The survey also turned up such general—but certainly pertinent—information for that particular fashion season as: bright colors should dominate the fall line; light and dark greens would be popular; blue would be a strong color; black and dark brown would sell better in the East and Southeast than in other areas.

Information like that obtained in these surveys is the raw material of planning. It is the information which can replace personal prejudice at the conference table. It gives the manufacturer a firm base for his color decisions, for making up his mind which colors to sell and where to sell them.

HOW COLOR SURVEYS ARE PLANNED

The survey is a test boring into the country's opinion; like a test boring, if it is done well it will produce useful results.

The key to the survey is the sample—the group of people you plan to poll. If you poll a good sample you can extrapolate from your results and talk with authority about what the huge group of people you didn't poll want. If you get a bad sample you can talk about nothing but what the sample wants; if you try to extrapolate from that you'll come a cropper, much as the *Literary Digest* did in its famous 1936 poll which predicted Landon would be elected president.

The people most concerned with polling—Dr. George Gallup, Ernest Dichter and A. C. Nielsen, for example—find that a survey must meet two tests:

It must be *reliable*—that is, it must give consistent, unambiguous results.

It must be *valid*—that is, it must measure what it's supposed to measure.

We achieve reliability and validity by selecting our sample from that specific group of people whom we can expect to buy the manufacturer's product. We divide our sample by geographic location, income group, sex, and occupation, aiming to set up a microcosm of the manufacturer's potential consumer market. Through this careful preorganization of our sample, we find that, in our specialized field, a sample of 2,400 gives us a valid and reliable result.

31

Since our questions are largely in the nature of "Which of these colors do you like best?" we are not faced with the pitfalls in wording which so often dog our less specialized polling brethren. However, we still have to pretest our questions to find out whether they contain any latent ambiguities which can scuttle our results.

One of the biggest pitfalls that we try to avoid is the use of color names—I've seen color surveys conducted by huge concerns which asked the persons interviewed to choose among lists of color names, all of which must have meant different things to different people. We get around this by showing our interviewees actual color swatches. One of the most ticklish jobs of the color engineer is preparing these swatches.

One recent survey by a leading institute showed that about 80 per cent of the men tested and 60 per cent of the women remembered "dark blue" better than any other color. What this institute didn't know is that there are over thirteen thousand variations of "dark blue," some high on the scale of remembrance, others very low. This research firm subsequently recommended that a certain client's ads be printed on "dark blue"—using black ink, of course! Did you ever try to read black ink on "dark blue"?

A SAMPLE SET OF QUESTIONS

Here are the questions and interview directions for a typical color-preference survey. This example is tailored to the hypothetical job of finding out which colors people like best for the interiors and exteriors of their homes. In administering the questionnaire, the interviewer refers the interviewee to a number of cards, each swatched with numbered color swatches.

INTERVIEWER: Write correct number in box where applicable.

INTERIOR:

1. Which of the nine colors shown on Card I (eight colors or white) do you prefer for your kitchen? (VOTE ONE CHOICE) ☐

2. Do you want kitchen flooring to be light or dark in color?
   (VOTE ONE CHOICE)
   A. LIGHT   ☐
   B. DARK   ☐

3. Would you like kitchen equipment (refrigerator, stove, sink) in color, either matching or contrasting with kitchen wall colors? (VOTE ONE CHOICE)
   A. I DO want equipment in color   ☐
   B. I DON'T want equipment in color   ☐

4. Which of the nine colors shown on Card I do your prefer for your dinette? (VOTE ONE CHOICE)   ☐

5. Which of the eight colors on Card II do you prefer for your living room? (VOTE ONE CHOICE)   ☐

6. If you prefer two colors for different living-room walls, which two colors on Card II do you prefer? (VOTE TWO CHOICES)   ☐☐

   (If prefers only one wall color in living room, check here.)   ☐

7. Which of the eight colors on Card III do you prefer for the master bedroom? (VOTE ONE CHOICE)   ☐

8. If you prefer two colors for different master-bedroom walls, which two colors on Card III do you prefer? (VOTE TWO CHOICES)   ☐☐

   (If prefers only one wall color in bedroom, check here.)   ☐

9. Which of the eight colors on Card IV do you prefer for the smaller bedroom? (VOTE ONE CHOICE)   ☐

10. Which of the six color alternatives on Card V (five colors or white) do you prefer for bathroom? (VOTE ONE CHOICE)   ☐

11. Which of the following interior features of the home would you prefer in a trim color varying from the wall colors? (VOTE AS MANY CHOICES AS DESIRED; IF NO TRIM COLOR IS WANTED IN HOME INTERIOR, CHECK BOX G.)
    A. Doors   ☐
    B. Door Frames   ☐
    C. Window Frames   ☐

33

      D. Cabinets □
      E. Cabinets and Closet Interiors □
      F. Floorboard □
      G. No trim color wanted □

12. Which of the nine colors on Card VI would you prefer for interior trim? (VOTE ONE CHOICE) □

13. Which of nine colors shown on Card VII (eight colors or white) do you prefer for ceilings? (VOTE ONE CHOICE) □

14. If you want a separate ceiling color for one or both bedrooms, which two colors on Card VII do you prefer? (VOTE TWO CHOICES) □□

(If wants only one ceiling color throughout, check here.) □

15. Which of the eight colors on Card VIII do you prefer for your flooring? (VOTE ONE CHOICE) □

16. If you want more than one flooring color, which two colors on Card VIII do you prefer? (VOTE TWO CHOICES) □□

(If wants only one flooring color throughout, check here.) □

EXTERIOR:

17. Which of the eleven colors shown for exterior walls do you prefer? (VOTE ONE CHOICE) □

18. Which of the nine colors shown for exterior trim do you prefer? (VOTE ONE CHOICE) □

19. In which of the outside areas mentioned below would you want to use an exterior trim color? (VOTE AS MANY CHOICES AS DESIRED; IF NO TRIM COLOR IS WANTED ON HOME EXTERIOR, CHECK BOX E.)
      A. Doors □
      B. Porch Area □
      C. Triangular Gable-End □
      D. Bay Window and Window Frames □
      E. No Trim Color Wanted □

20. Would you want venetian blinds to match color of exterior window trim? (CHECK ONE CHOICE)
    A. Yes ☐
    B. No ☐

21. Which of nine colors shown for roofing do you prefer? (VOTE ONE CHOICE) ☐

22. Check age group (INTERVIEWER ASK):
    A. Under 30 ☐
    B. 30 to 45 ☐
    C. 45-plus ☐

23. Check income group (INTERVIEWER ESTIMATE):
    A. Under $4,200 ☐
    B. $4,200–7,000 ☐
    E. $7,000-plus ☐

24. Check area:
    A. New England ☐
    B. Mid-Atlantic ☐
    C. Southeast ☐
    D. Midwest ☐
    E. North Central ☐
    F. Mississippi Valley ☐
    G. Southwest ☐
    H. Pacific Coast ☐

HOW TO USE THE SURVEY

Once this information is all in and tabulated, the color engineer is faced with a neat IBM-typewritten summary of preferences on his desk. So far, so good, but so far is not very far. For the polling of people and the tabulation of their answers is only the first step in the color engineer's survey. His next job, and it it a tough one, is interpreting and analyzing the results.

He has to consider several factors in this analysis:

The swatch effect. Colors don't look the same on a swatch and, for instance, on a wall. Hence not only does the color engineer have to consider and compensate for this discrepancy

35

when he makes up his swatches, but he will have to apply the discrepancy to his interpretation of results. He knows, better than the average interviewee, how to visualize the way the various colors will appear in each end use contemplated.

The sample effect. The color engineer polls the prospective market for a particular group of colors in a particular application. It may be that the introduction of new colors will bring a host of new and unexpected customers into that market. This means that in analyzing the results from his sample the color engineer must worry not only about what the people included in the sample wanted, but what those who weren't included probably would have wanted. In doing this, he must draw on the statistical information he has gleaned from concurrent surveys on related products aimed at a somewhat different market.

The interview effect. Social psychologists also call this the "halo effect"; what they mean is that the very process of being interviewed may modify the consumer's opinions so that he tells not what he wants, but what he thinks the interviewer wants him to want. We counteract this effect by building linked questions into the questionnaire, then applying discrepancies in the answers to our interpretation of results.

When he finishes this process the color engineer can tell you a multitude of things. He can give you information on color, and color's associate, design, which will enable you to:

1. Find preference for color of a product.
2. Find design preference.
3. Find pattern preference.
4. Find texture preference.
5. Find bottle or package preference.
6. Determine form of product consumers prefer.
7. Discover features desired in a new product.
8. See if information on a label is meaningful.
9. Discover how product is used.
10. Determine the need for new products and color.

11. Help pick a name for a product.
12. Disclose seasonal differences in use of product.
13. Determine variations in use of products and colors in different localities.
14. Determine variations in product and color use by sex, education, economic group.
15. Find new uses for old products.
16. Find out whether new product and colors are liked by dealer.
17. Find out if they are liked by consumer.
18. Check on effectiveness of sales displays.
19. Analyze color effectiveness of present outlets.
20. Find out exactly what happens color-wise at point of sale.
21. Anticipate future color trends.
22. Determine color-buying motivations.
23. Discover new sales ideas for product.
24. Determine what colors are helping your competition.
25. Determine effectiveness of company's color personality.

Of course not every survey is going to give you all this information. But this is the type of information you can get. How would you like to have it by your elbow when you start worrying about your next year's plans?

All color and design planning must start with the customer. The customer is always right. If enough of the customers decide that next year they want a three-wheeled car, you had better start building one. If they want their milk colored green, you'd better do something about your cow's diet. Consumer preference, a wayward, shifting, unsettled, and persnickety thing, can run up your profits or put you out of business. It all depends upon how closely you keep tabs on that preference, and the one best way is through the survey.

In setting up a survey, it is of vital importance to select colors only in relation to what is known to be appropriate, effective, and durable for the product. Otherwise, the results

37

might suggest choices that are completely unfeasible or pro-hibitively costly for a particular product or market. To confront an interviewee with a large, haphazard selection of colors and expect him to accurately visualize how they'd look in a finished room or an airplane exterior is tempting fate.

It's an important truism that in color surveys and selections, more mistakes are made from lack of facts than from faulty judgment or poor taste.

WHAT YOU CAN LEARN ABOUT COLOR
FROM SUPERMARKETS

You have to be in Montreal to see or believe how color and Steinberg's chain of supermarkets help each other. Some supermarket chains use the same color scheme in all their stores. But Steinberg's—Canada's most successful—has no two alike. And the Steinberg emphasis on color pays off handsomely; the chain beats $100 million in annual sales.

The Steinberg lesson is that professional color engineering in store planning is growing more and more important each year. Today color planning—and its close cousin, illumination engineering—is a major factor in store design. Appropriate color symbols tag different departments; selected colors improve product appearance, boost sales, and cut returns of merchandise.

COLOR: PRIME PRODUCT MOVER

Whether merchandise in a store wins or loses customer appeal depends on how that merchandise looks to the customer. Today progressive merchandisers, working with stores large or small, understand and use the sales impact that correct color planning can provide for their wares.

The importance of well-planned sales appeal is obvious, especially in periods of buyers' markets. Recent factual surveys reveal that:

1. More and more buyers are becoming color-conscious.
2. The American eye has become adjusted to color.

Consequently, color's influence in store styling assumes more and more importance every year.

Although it lacks shape, size, and weight, and must have proper light, color is becoming the most important single merchandising force in store operation today. It controls the appearance of everything we see. It governs our reactions. We have only to close our eyes or turn out the lights to sense the flatness of life without color. Nothing in nature gives us more immediate or varied pleasure than the perception of color. Few things speak more directly to our senses.

A skillful use of color can give a store personality. Yet few stores take advantage of this fact. Except for the name on the outside of the store, almost any chain-store customer would be unable to tell you what chain he's in.

Many of these stores retain ineffectual white. Some go along, hit or miss, without qualified guidance, using burnt plum or sick gray or other nondescript shades. These methods sacrifice the chance to build a store personality. They fly in the face of recent studies which show that 80 per cent of consumer buying depends on impulse appeal, and that in impulse appeal color is the prime mover.

The stark, sterile, spiritless, glaring white store interior ignores this selling value of color. So does the store painted in nondescript colors. Even worse is the store "decorated" without regard to the primary job of selling its wares. Some time ago a *Saturday Evening Post* article talked about the latest advances in supermarket design. A few weeks later the magazine printed a letter from an irate shopper saying that supermarkets needed "not fountains and flowers and colored lights" but "eating food." That customer was right. Successful color planning will use the fountains and flowers and colored lights not as haphazard, cheap, and tawdry gimmicks, competing with the selling job of your store, but as careful sales techniques to underline and give special new importance to the "eating" in that unhappy consumer's plea for "eating food."

(The key to building a profit-making store personality is color engineering.) The color engineer builds on facts instead of fancies in developing his color recommendations—in developing market colors that don't annoy but sell. It takes years of practical experience—plus an innate ability to plan and use colors—to engineer a store color plan that can stir without disturbing.

In preparing a color plan, three factors must be considered:

1. Suitability to the merchandise.
2. Harmony of colors.
3. Illumination suited both to the merchandise and background colors.

Success in planning the over-all appearance of a store lies in the proper employment of one or more of the basic families. When he uses these families in various appealing but unusual relationships, there is absolutely no limit to the variety of good color schemes the color engineer can create. Attractive color individuality can give a store a distinctive trade-mark and create a buying atmosphere. Capable color styling in a store can help win a competitor's customers.

PSYCHOLOGY IN COLOR SELLING

Distinction and beauty in color choice, however, are not enough to give stores the full value of color's vast potential. Profitable color use also depends on psychology—the association of color with certain ideas, such as red with "danger." Color has a remarkably uniform influence on our psychological reactions. In developing a color plan, therefore, it is desirable to determine first the mood you want to establish in your customers, then to select the colors that will best produce this mood.

Different colors affect most people as follows:

Red excites.　　　　　　　　　*Green refreshes.*
Pink and peach appetize.　　　*Blue cools and subdues.*
Orange activates.　　　　　　 *Purple depresses.*
Yellow cheers.　　　　　　　　*Magenta stimulates.*

In all successful color planning these psychological aspects of color are capably and constantly brought into play. For example, the implication of hot food will be conveyed by the use of red, a warm color; we suggest freshness with green, which from time immemorial people have associated with vegetation. Cold objects can best be depicted by blue since blue is traditionally considered a cold color. Thus, you should consider the individual business-building aspects of each of these color attributes as they concern your store—both the exterior and the interior. The next time you modernize the department selling, say, bed sheets, try using sky blue. It will serve to make the sheets look even whiter. This is the same merchandising technique utilized by the old farmer who packed his white eggs in blue-lined containers to emphasize their clean, snowy look.

CONTRAST: KEY COLOR TOOL

Here is another important factor in color planning: colors cannot be readily distinguished, one from the other, without proper contrast. You can obtain color contrast in only four ways:

1. Use a light value of a color against a dark value of a color or vice versa—pink on maroon, for example.
2. Use a weak chroma of a color against a strong chroma of a color, or vice versa—strong emerald green against pale grayed green.

42

3. Use a warm color against a cold color, or vice versa—orange on blue-green.
4. Use a color against its complement—red on green; yellow on purple-blue.

In planning store backgrounds, lettering, price tags, truck markings, and display cards, you should bear in mind the excellent legibility and noticeability you can obtain by employing maximum contrast. For example, dark-value pure purple-blue on pale grayed yellow creates contrast entailing:

1. low value and high value
2. color and its complement
3. a warm color and a cold color
4. a grayed color with a pure color

Here then are all four components of strong contrast. But the color scheme will lack the highly desirable ingredient of unusualness. It's still better to use unexpected color combinations, such as lime yellow and blue, chartreuse and coral pink, or orange and green.

It is the *unusually* pleasant color scheme that will build personality and distinction for a store. Having been a color engineer to American business and industry for more than twenty years, I can say from abundant experience that color and light are vitally important to the conduct of your store. When adequately applied, color can attract customers and increase sales.

CHOOSING COLORS CORRECTLY

Color expertly used in stores—not nondescript color that contributes nothing or "decorator" color that may distract—color correctly chosen to do its job and correctly applied to the areas that call for it can *stir without disturbing*. Color in a store can provide subtle stimulation without distracting a working force from its duties or patrons from the merchandise. The right colors and their arrangement can make a small store appear

43

larger, a large store appear smaller, a narrow store seem wider, or a too-deep store seem better proportioned.

Color correctly selected and applied can change the apparent shape of a room, or departmentalize different areas in a large room, without the use of partitions. Merely changing the color of a key display gondola from white to gold can sufficiently accent its presence so that it compels greater attention and provides more impulse motivation. Store walls and fixtures can complement each other in color, giving an over-all pleasing effect and improving the buying atmosphere of the store.

Here are some suggestions for colors for various store departments, listing those colors that will set off merchandise to the best advantage.

MERCHANDISE	TYPE OF COLOR	EFFECTS DESIRED
Furs	Soft, cool—blue or blue-green	Suggesting winter in contrast to warm tones of furs
Better Dresses	Warm, light shades—mixed colors like mauve, chartreuse, and oyster white	Sophisticated, subtle tones, but warm and flattering to complexion
Low-Price Dresses	Same as above, but less grayed shades of color—beige, rose, warm green	To set off bright-colored dresses
Jewelry	Walls light but grayed; showcases in black, dark blue, or dark brown	Deep, rich colors to set off brightness of jewelry
Cosmetics	Pinks, grays, whites	Light colors that contrast or tone-in with packages for cosmetics
Women's Shoes	Clear light colors—greens, blues, yellows, beige	To set off darker shoe tones
Men's Shoes	Deeper shades of definite color—green, blue, rust	To contrast with tan or black of shoes

44

What You Can Learn About Color from Supermarkets

MERCHANDISE	TYPE OF COLOR	EFFECTS DESIRED
Children's Shoes	Variants of primaries—red, blue, yellow	Bright, cheerful effect
Radios	Blue, green, yellow, off-white	Dark shades where radios are light; lighter shades with dark-wood cabinets to induce cheerful, receptive mood
Kitchenware	White, green, medium blue, red	Cheerful, stimulating, and appetizing
Baby's Department	Pastel shades of any color	May range from light shades to medium-dark; darker shades should be kept slightly grayed
Lingerie	Pastel shades	Medium-light in any color except pinks or whites, since those are most popular lingerie colors and would not show up against such backgrounds
Home Furnishings	Any popular decorators' colors	To show how furnishings would look in current room settings
Millinery	Beige, grays, pinks, mauves	Soft, flattering shades
Men's Furnishings	Gray-green, gray-blue, royal blue, maroon, tan, red	Strong masculine colors
Food	Peach, pink, green, and yellow	Appetizing colors

WHERE DO STORE COLORS COME FROM?

Too often a store's color, like Topsy, "just growed." Colors have a way of working their way into your store without your noticing them, but just because you don't notice them doesn't mean that the colors are working for your profit.

The colors in your store appear from eight sources:

1. paint   5. draperies
2. lighting   6. fixtures
3. floor covering 7. product color
4. wall finish   8. packages

The store's color engineer can entirely control all of these color sources except product and package. He can develop new wall colors and design new lighting and prescribe new fixtures. But how about product and package? They are what matters. When all is said and done, it's his wares that the store operator worries about. If he can't control their color, why should he bother with the rest? The answer can have a dramatic dollars-and-cents impact on your sales. For of course the color engineer *can* control the display setting for merchandise colors. He can make food look more appetizing, larger, and fresher. He can make appliances look better-built, and enhance the appearance of fabrics. More and more stores are learning a double lesson, and learning it to their profit:

Prescribe profitable color wherever you can; use a distinctive color plan for your floors, walls, and lighting. It costs no more to use color skillfully.

Enhance and capitalize on colors when you can't prescribe them; show off your merchandise and its packaging and cash in on its natural sales appeal.

HOW THE COLOR ENGINEER WORKS

In developing profitable color for your store the color engineer plans his work to answer a series of questions:

1. *What is the function of your color plan?*

The answer to this question is short and straight forward: to sell merchandise.

2. What are the conditions of your store's use?

To answer this the color engineer must consider the nature and buying habits of the consumer in your specific store and its neighborhood; the hours the store is open; the layout of counters and displays; the method the consumer uses in selecting his merchandise and the store uses in checking that merchandise out; the products you want to emphasize. These are but a few of the scores of factors the color engineer feeds into his hopper of color facts in analyzing the problem of how to prescribe color for your store.

3. What color and designs do competitors employ?

Here the color engineer is not only concerned with keeping posted on the color techniques your competitor is using to boost sales, but, more important, is building you a distinctive store personality—the impersonal stamped-from-a-mold store is passing up a valuable chance to plant a selling personality in the minds of its customers.

4. Where will colors be applied in the store?

Here the color engineer examines your store from the standpoint of architecture and layout. He determines what materials, finishes, lighting units, and fixtures can profit from color planning, and in what locations and relationships the colors developed for this color plan best build sales.

5. What psychological relationships are involved?

The color engineer must deal here with the mechanics of a consumer's buying, with the motivation that will make the shopper buy one pair of socks instead of another, a ketchup bottle from a pile rather than from a shelf, an electric mixer under one type of light rather than the same mixer under another. Here the color planner employs the important concepts of color harmony and association, drawing on his knowledge of: (a) the colors people feel are in *harmony*—those colors that experience has taught him enhance each other in mutually effective visual relationships; (b) the colors people *associate* with good merchandise or with a particular type of merchandise.

47

6. *What background colors require consideration?*

The consumer does not see your wares on their own, floating in space against an invisible background. He sees merchandise in company with other merchandise, with display cases, floor coverings, walls, windows, and even other customers as its background. Just making a piece of meat or a bottle of perfume or a cashmere sweater attractive on its own is not enough. Every item displayed in your store must be analyzed in terms of its background, and both the display and the background lighted and colored accordingly.

7. *Under what lighting conditions should your wares be viewed?*

All merchandise is seen under some form of natural and/or artificial light. Many present-day light sources break up and waste the useful and attractive colors that purchasers associate with good merchandise; careless or haphazard lighting can make your wares look shoddy, ill-made, and tawdry.

Once the color engineer has answered these seven questions, he goes to work on a specific color and lighting plan for your store, always bearing in mind that his target is selling—helping build business. He develops new and profitable colors for walls, draperies, floor coverings, and fixtures; he designs and specifies a lighting layout that will put color-corrected light to work in increasing the visual appeal of all of your merchandise presentations. The result is a store full of well-lighted and attractively colored products, and a well-lighted and attractively colored product is a product that is more than 80 per cent sold.

SUPERMARKETS: COLOR SELLING IN ACTION

One of the best examples of the impact of modern color planning on selling is the supermarket. Supermarkets are fast learning the merchandising value of correct color. The author has developed color plans for such successful chains as The Kroger Company, American Stores Company, Steinberg's

Limited, First National Stores, and Food Fair, Inc. But there are still many supermarkets today which haven't gotten the word.

Most supermarkets are still painted "sanitary" white—a color considered to have some natural association with the selling of food, but one which in reality lends a cold, clinical, impersonal, institutional look to a marketplace where warmth, cheer, and hominess are more in order.

White, of course, is showing up less and less in today's kitchens, today's appliances, today's interior-decoration schemes. The trend in the home now is definitely to related colors. This is one of the most important things for anyone in the super-market field to remember. For if women want color in their homes, they will equally want color in the store.

It has always been a source of astonishment to me that super-market operators who lavish so much thought on the layout, engineering, and design of their new markets rarely give the same attention to the use of color. Color stands in a corner like a forsaken orphan and its use is often entrusted to people who know nothing of its proper employment and merchandising value. This situation is unfortunate because color can often make or break the appeal which the supermarket operator tries so hard to achieve.

A cold, depressing shade of blue can destroy an otherwise cheerful shopping atmosphere. A bad choice of yellow can nauseate, just as a good choice of yellow can add to the appetite appeal of a supermarket. To make the market a desirable place in which to shop, this knowledge of the effect of color on people must be put to work intelligently. It costs no more to use the right color—it requires no more labor, no more paint. This being the case, it is certainly worth while for the supermarket operator to learn the right way to use color productively.

In applying color to supermarkets, our aim should be: (1) to attract attention; (2) to please the eye; (3) to sell more mer-chandise; (4) to emphasize the individuality and character of the market.

49

SUPERMARKET COLOR STYLING

Let's look at an example of store color planning in action—my plan for the Kroger Company's 1,450 stores. Here is a new way to increase impulse appeal by introducing color styling and merchandising innovations featuring original wallpaper murals that identify Kroger food departments, and are co-ordinated with the store color plan. The special wallpapers implement four big sales objectives: (1) merchandising Kroger brands, (2) stepping up impulse buying, (3) imparting home-like atmosphere that builds traffic, (4) reducing maintenance (wallpapering costs less than repainting). For example, fresh produce display cases are identified and highlighted by the wall-paper depicting a cornucopia spilling out luscious fruits and vegetables. Another wallpaper identifying the meat department handsomely dramatizes in one integrated, eye-appealing area the various meat animals. Appetizing colors, coral and turquoise, harmonize throughout the store interior and give merchandise and service an impressive, memorable corporate identity.

Kroger ordinarily sells for lower prices than the leading competitors in most areas in the twenty-one-state Kroger terri-tory. Therefore the impulse-building momentum of featuring on walls the leading Kroger food items is bound to up sales. In fact, Kroger sales increased 18 per cent in 1957.

Through adroit color planning and co-ordination, you can achieve a realistically new-appearing store environment that is spacious, restful—and has compelling feminine appeal—with-out the excessive costs entailed in resorting to structural changes.

More examples of specific applications of color engineering to the supermarket are worth including here. These are drawn from my work for The American Stores Company. Many of the innovations were developed in close co-operation with such appliance manufacturers as the Tyler Refrigeration Corpora-tion.

Store Number 1 has a high gabled ceiling to the rear with lowered ceiling areas in other parts of the store. My color plan took advantage of this unique architecture by emphasizing the unusual design. A slightly greenish blue-sky ceiling under the gable accents a novel spray of sunburst lighting; a soft pink on the lowered parts of the ceiling gives the high light reflectance needed over cases and counters. One of the big problems with this high-ceilinged store was pulling customers through it. A large mural under the gable does the job; it uses a new, large-pattern wallpaper especially created for supermarkets. The floor of this store is lined out with strips of gray and coral and large areas of solid colors—the pattern sets up natural paths for customers to follow through the store.

Store Number 2 is wide rather than long—again there is the problem of pulling customers into the store. Here dark blue walls above the height of the wall cases tend to draw the customer toward a colorful contrasting green on the rear wall where the meat counters are located. This dark-bright combination also makes the store look longer and narrower. To avoid monotony the blue walls are not identical—one is wallpapered with showy dishes, fruits, and flowers on a blue ground while the other is a solid color of matching blue. The counters and wall cases carry out the same color plan with a single bright accent near the rear of the store; there the profit-producing fish and meat cases use a soft red, a color keyed to tie in with a similar red in the wallpaper pattern and developed to enhance the visual attractiveness of the counters' contents.

Store Number 3 is also wide instead of long. Here another color-engineering technique is used to make the store look longer and pull customers to the rear. The back wall is a cool light blue, suggesting distance and size. This blue is taken up in the meat, fish, and poultry cases—it is an excellent color for emphasizing product freshness. The frozen-food cases are a creamy ivory, a color developed to allow the store operator to take advantage of the high inherent sales appeal of these colorfully packaged products.

Store Number 4 uses still another approach. Here, with no architectural problem, the theme of the store is carried out

51

with a wallpaper emphasizing food products. The display cases pick up and repeat the wall colors. The meat counters are a light green—still another excellent display color for meat—and the ice-cream cases a festive and appetizing pink. One innovation in this store is the introduction of American Olean tile behind the meat counter—there is no substitute for the appearance and cleanliness of tile.

Here, then, are four additional specific solutions to the store operator's sensible question: How can color help me sell? One lesson these experiences teach us is that there is never a pat, uniform solution. One store's successful meat counter can be another store's sales poison. Each store has its own problems. Each store has its own characteristics of architecture and layout. Each store has its own type of customer and each customer his own peculiarities.

COLOR ON FLOORS

One theme running through these examples is the special importance of floor coloring. Too many stores slap down flooring without adequate consideration for the important contribution a proper floor surface color can make. A floor can reflect or absorb light. It can complement the décor of the store, inflict a hideous discord, or merely be innocuous.

In my work for stores, particularly the store chains, I have designed flooring to help guide the patron subconsciously to displays of high-profit merchandise—party foods, for example. As can be seen, there is more to flooring than that which meets the tread of the trade. Colorful flooring, effectively planned, can do much to brighten the interior of any store as well as reflect light more efficiently and camouflage dust.

GENERAL HINTS ON STORE COLOR

The general color plan developed for a store must underscore the relationship between the store's various selling floors and among its specialized departments. A color plan relating all interior areas sets a tone with the initial impression it creates as a customer enters the store. It maintains this tone in a harmonious treatment throughout. Special accent coloring provides dramatic punch for specific items or display areas; it employs a color intensity many times that of nearby areas and capitalizes on colors which dramatize the particular merchandise shown. Display coloring calls the attention of the customer to related items or groups of items on display, in showcases or open racks.

In all cases, store-interior colors are effective only when they call attention to merchandise rather than to themselves. I have seen business increase 14 per cent within a month after a store's interior and exterior were properly color-engineered. This is by no means an isolated case. Good color gives a store, any store, personality and prestige. It is possible, of course, to use color to endow a low-price store with an uptown atmosphere. This is a misguided use; such a color plan could easily discourage trade. It is therefore important to be judicious in one's choice and use of colors for store styling. The trend today is toward linking store styling to neighborhood and geographical considerations rather than trying to employ a standard décor regardless of special needs or sectional peculiarities.

UNITY WITHOUT UNIFORMITY

Using related color plans in all store units in a chain operation creates a profitable recognition value as consumers see the outlets in different cities; at the same time it sets up the impression of a vast central buying power which can mean savings to the consumer. As is noted in the previous section, this standardization should not be carried to the point at which desirable variations in accordance with regional or local tastes or customs are overlooked.

An example of this unity without uniformity is seen in the styling of the nineteen thousand service stations operated by the

Cities Service Oil Company. Prior to my assignment to modernize the appearance of these stations, they represented a limitless variety of architectural styles, with their only common denominator a spiritless black and white color scheme. It was obviously uneconomic to attempt extensive redesign and rebuilding of station structures to obtain similarity; instead I created a new styling concept for this firm through color. A very special bluish green and a bluish red, combined with a white incorporating a slight bluish undertone, made a most distinctive color ensemble. The bluish undertone gave the white paint a special bright whiteness that helped to make the stations appear larger, more modern, and neater. These colors provided maximum contrast and enabled the stations to stand out and attract the eyes of passing motorists. Durability was a fundamental consideration in developing these colors for outdoor use, and I prepared the paint specifications to insure that the Cities Service colors would be uniform throughout the stations and on all products. High-quality paints and finishes, carefully prescribed, can frequently impart extra value by lengthening repainting-maintenance intervals.

Excess ornamentation and less appealing structural features which added to the disquieting variety of the stations' structural stylings were camouflaged by an all-white treatment. Outmoded cathedral-type arched windows were squared off with plywood inserts and the inserts painted.

Unity for this chain of stations was further heightened by the introduction of the new Cities Service Green in striping and lettering on the station signs and exteriors. The color plan was applied to pumps, trade-marks, emblems, and packaged-goods containers. It now appears on company-owned vehicles, tank trucks, railroad tank cars, the oceangoing tanker fleet, and uniforms, and is supported in the company's advertising campaigns.

The special Cities Service Red was introduced in only one spot on the station apron—on the premium-grade fuel pumps. As a *Reader's Digest* article announced after the color styling was finished, this color spotlighting raised sales of premium-grade fuel by as much as 50 per cent. A gas station is a very special kind of store. Color engineering certainly brought ample added sales volume to this store's merchandise.

DISPLAY COLORS SELL

The management of chain-store units today must seek identity, prestige, and merchandising advantages through the use of distinctive and appropriate colors in display areas.

Direction and distance of display coloring from the merchandise is crucial here; textures and colors of fabrics, for example, change appearance with changes in adjacent color areas. In the Fifth Avenue shop of New York's Bond Clothing Stores, I sought to apply the psychological factors discussed earlier in the chapter. Some colors are masculine, some feminine; some appeal to the young, some to the old; some are gay, some somber. In the Bond Store's little girls' department I used the bright colors which appeal to the young. Fitting rooms for rosy-cheeked youngsters were colored to appeal to the eye of the very-junior miss; downstairs, fitting rooms for her mother and big sister were in warm, flattering rose colors. The wallpaper in the children's barbershop consisted of colored comics.

The first floor embraced both men's and women's departments; there colors of strong masculine appeal were used in the men's shop areas. A brilliant vermilion set the tone of this masculine province, in contrast to a deep wine red used in the women's sector. On the floors devoted to men alone, coppers and tans were the basic colors, while turquoise, rose, and bone white supplied a rich feminine atmosphere on a women's floor.

In applying color as a selling tool for this large clothing outlet, an outlet which may be expected to set the pace for other chains, a consistency of reds and blues was maintained through out the store, giving over-all unity while allowing variety within hues of individual shops.

LIGHTING ALSO SELLS

Color planning and lighting go hand in hand. We can develop correct colors for walls and floors, choose a careful display environment for our merchandise, select fixture colors and draperies engineered to sell. Unless we use the right lighting, all that work may go to waste.

Correct lighting shows phenomenal selling power. One food store operator watched his sales increase 20 per cent after he installed special lighting. A hardware store's sales climbed as much as 40 per cent. Gimbel's, in Philadelphia, restyled its piece-goods department to specifications set out in a coordinated color and lighting plan. The color-corrected lighting closely simulated daylight; sales-dollar volume doubled and returns fell off 60 per cent.

Current commercial interest in lighting shows up in a recent survey. The study reports that lighting changes figure in 75 per cent of store rehabilitation planning. A poll of women's page editors indicates that 48 per cent of the editors demand better store lighting.

Department-store operators in particular are facing up to this problem of increasing sales through proper illumination. They know that every type of merchandise is best displayed under a particular quality of light.

Properly developed lighting plans, engineered individually for the specific conditions peculiar to each store, will do much to:

Speed the sale
Keep the sale sold
Help insure leadership for both product and sponsor

PROPER LIGHTING
ENHANCES PRODUCT APPEARANCE

The toughest test for a lighting plan is our old friend the supermarket. Food appearance is paramount in helping the consumer decide whether she's going to buy that food or go to some other store.

Color-corrected light can make meats look their true prime best. It can bring out the garden-fresh appearance of produce. When I went to work on The Kroger Company's stores there was no such color-corrected light. It took a radical new lighting fixture to do the job.

The fixture I designed brings out the true colors of food in the most candid and undistorted way. The fluorescent-lamp housing in this fixture is equipped with a perforated aluminum baffle, permitting some of the light to come through but directing *most* of it down into the merchandise displays. To offset the fact that the whitest fluorescent lamps on the market today cast a light that is a trifle blue, the lamp deflector is enameled with a certain shade of warm ivory. The light reflected from this ivory surface picks up a warm tinge—the resultant total light cast is *white* instead of bluish, as it would have been had not color correction been provided.

This color-corrected lighting does its job to perfection throughout the entire store. It distorts no type of merchandise. The white suet on fresh meat, for example, remains white— not yellowed as it is under incandescent light or warm white fluorescent light. The meat itself looks invitingly fresh and appetizing.

On the produce counters, the fruits and vegetables appear as mouth-watering as if they were growing in sunlit gardens. Baked goods and multicolored packages and containers, no longer distorted by improper lighting, appear at their palatable best.

One special problem in my supermarket work concerned the cellophane wrappings now used generally for precut meat. Cellophane is never water-white, or truly colorless—it sets up a surface distortion that causes a loss of visual depth. Only when it is penetrated by the right intensity of properly color-corrected light will the consumer see her meat without distortion.

Incandescent floodlights (without color correction) proved

to be the answer. They were blended with the color-corrected fluorescent lights of the general store lighting plan. The result was the additional depth needed to penetrate the cellophane.

Lighting engineers who inspect work for Kroger are continually astonished with the success of the installation. At the Kroger Market on Detroit's Davison Avenue their light meters registered extraordinary foot-candle readings of 110 at the top of display counters. With two out of the four lamps in each color-corrected unit off, the foot-candle reading was still 54. At the floor of the store, with all four lamps in a unit operating, the foot-candle reading was 60 plus.

HOW MUCH LIGHT AND WHERE?

The aim of the illumination engineer is to put light where light is necessary. At the same time he has to be careful to develop a lighting plan which permits store managers to arrange their displays in any location. This is the answer to the store manager's economically sound complaint that highly specialized and inflexible lighting makes it expensive and difficult to rearrange displays conveniently.

Some stores suffer from too little light—they are spiritless and drab. But another prime concern of the illumination engineer is the store with too much light. Too much light is just as damaging as too little. High levels of illumination require high reflectance on working, fixture, and product surfaces. Without this high reflectance the brightness ratio between light source and the object to be seen is too great for working and shopping comfort, convenience and efficiency.

Most supermarkets today, for example, are lighted so that they assault their customers at the entrance to the store with a blast of light directly in the eyes. I call this assault "cotton in the eyes"; it is exactly the reverse of the sensation you get when you walk into a dark movie theater and find you can't see the seats. As far as food sales go, cotton in the eyes is cash out of pocket for the supermarket operator. The strong lighting makes his merchandise harder to see, not easier. The illumination engineer designs his prescription lighting to insure an evenly lit, glareless store. No customer entering such a store is assaulted by glare and the attendant discomfort which too often makes marketing a chore.

COLOR AFFECTS LIGHTING, TOO

Correct lighting complements and sets off to best advantage the colors in your store and its merchandise. And the converse is true—color can often compensate for unsatisfactory lighting conditions. For example, the warm sunlight of a southern exposure, if unwanted, can be counteracted by painting your store interior in cool blues or blue-greens. Tans, beiges, and pinks will bring warmth to the cool light of a northern exposure.

This adds up to the necessity for close co-ordination between light and color in your store. Department-store operators understand the need for this co-ordination. They know, for example, that the intense illumination which shows hard goods to advantage is not so flattering to women's apparel. They have learned that pink induces women to try on apparel more readily, and they combine pink-cast soft-white fluorescent tubes with pink wall-color treatments, carpets, or draperies.

This close relationship between color and lighting is even more important in the completely self-service store. For there the products must sell themselves.

CONSIDER THE EMPLOYEE

Color and lighting are important to you and your customers, and they are equally important to the people who work in your store. Today, forward-looking store operators choose careful color and lighting plans not only to boost sales but to promote efficiency and safety for their workers.

Restful colors on walls and high-reflectance colors on ceilings can substantially reduce eyestrain. When eyestrain decreases, physical fatigue follows suit and up goes efficiency. As we shall

59

see in more detail in the next chapter, the color engineer further increases worker efficiency by using certain brilliant colors to signal danger areas—something to think about when you touch up that loading platform, work area, or stock room.

One important consideration here: our visual acuity at eighteen is usually double what it will be at sixty. If older eyes are at work, you will need to employ a much higher level of lighting intensity.

FEATURES OF PROPER LIGHTING

We have seen that different types of artificial light sources produce different color qualities of light. For this reason, lighting recommendations for stores should be predicated upon the use of *right* sources—lamps of exactly the right color temperature to insure maximum efficiency with minimum glare. Prescription lighting fixtures, individually designed and intelligently selected and skillfully prescribed for each individual seeing task, will provide the needed intensity, uniformity, and color correction essential to success in today's competitive selling arena.

For a store, proper fluorescent lighting will provide:

Higher intensity
More even distribution of light
Improved color correction
Increased efficiency (more foot-candles per watt)
Improved "punch" in down-lighting
Better reflectance
More pleasing design of fixture
Less heat radiation

STORE COLOR AND LIGHTING:
THE FUTURE

I believe in the power of well-integrated design, color, and lighting to add something appreciable to the merchandising potentialities of American stores. I believe that as business conditions change, as sellers' and buyers' markets alternate with each other, the professional use of color with lighting to boost sales will become even more important than it is today. For the proper use of color, design, and lighting *invites the public in*. And without the proper invitation, business as usual is difficult to transact.

For the future, I myself look not so much to business as *usual,* but to business as *unusual*—a state of affairs in which the businessman can no longer afford to ignore the appeal, sales stimulation, and invitation that good color, design, and light can build into his store; a state of affairs in which the progressive local chain and individual store operator can excel and out-merchandise the national chains through correct color and properly planned lighting.

COLOR AND LIGHTING IN THE DISPLAY WINDOW

It takes a passer-by eleven seconds, give or take a few, to walk past your show window. That's all the time you have to convert him from a pedestrian into a shopper. The modern display window is the latter-day equivalent of the old street barker, the man with the derby who used to drag you by the arm and lead you inside to see the day's specials. Today you have to do the same job minus the man, minus the derby, minus the sales pitch, and with the further handicap of a slab of plate glass between you and the pedestrian. Fortunately you're armed with a pair of tools that makes the barker as obsolete as the five-cent beer: you guessed it—color and lighting.

The sales effectiveness—or lack of it—of your display window is going to meet a lot of people. Not long ago the Advertising Research Foundation ran off a study of pedestrian traffic in nineteen cities. From that study we have been able to draw some conclusions on how many people are going to pass by your display window:

If you sell in a small city with a population of from 15,000 to 25,000, then 10,000 to 15,000 people per week will pass your

62

window (assuming you're in the city's business district of course).

If you sell in a city of approximately 100,000 people, 40,000 to 50,000 pedestrians per week will pass your window.

If you sell in a city of 250,000 people, 60,000 to 70,000 pedestrians a week will pass your window.

If you live in a city exceeding 1,000,000 in population, you can expect more than 100,000 passers-by per week.

This is a king-sized audience. It is an audience that you can reach effectively through window display—at one of the lowest expenditures per prospective customer available to the businessman today. Even the smallest store can afford a sales-producing display window. The problem, naturally, is making sure that your display dollar gets maximum results.

The display man has seven tools at his disposal. These are:

1. Merchandise   4. Fixtures
2. Color   5. Material
3. Lighting   6. Props
     7. Display cards and copy

He aims to combine all these tools into an effective display, a selling display. These tools are all important; a good display will take advantage of every one of them. The trick is knowing how to use them. In this chapter we're going to discuss each tool, but we'll be concentrating on color and lighting. For it is with careful color adaptations and correct lighting that the store owner can convert his display from a storehouse on the street to a dynamic salesman.

MERCHANDISE

No matter what else goes into your window, your merchandise is the center of attention. That's what you want to sell. The four-step aim of the display window is (1) catching the passer-by's eye, (2) inducing him to look at your merchandise, (3) making him want to buy that merchandise (or making him remember that he wanted to buy it all along), then (4) bringing him into your store so he'll buy it from you.

Before we even talk about color and lighting, then, we must decide on the best arrangement for your merchandise.

Your window's display of merchandise is a small but representative catalogue of your wares. From looking at it the customer is going to form some firm opinions about the merchandise you're carrying inside your store, and about the kind of store you run. That means that your window should contain only items which can answer "yes" to three questions:

1. Is this item representative of what my store sells?

2. Is this item—because of price, appearance, style, or any other unique feature—the kind of item which a prospective customer will find especially appealing?

3. Does this item enhance the other merchandise in the window, and will its attractiveness be enhanced by other merchandise? A baby carriage in a window full of men's clothes would be ludicrous; each of your windows should have a central, guiding theme.

Once you have selected your merchandise in accordance with these qualifications, you're faced with the problem of finding the best possible arrangement for it. There are a number of considerations which must guide you here.

Pick out the one or two items in your window which you think have the best sales appeal, and make those the most prominent. The other merchandise in the window must not compete for visual power with those items. Theater people have a crafty technique called "upstaging"; you've seen it on TV when the bit player works his way between you and the leading lady. If you let subordinate merchandise upstage the more important items in your window you'll lose sales.

Avoid cluttering your window with a large number of items; many display designers, as a rule of thumb, limit themselves to a dozen. If you have too many things in the window, your prospective customer won't know where to look; by the time she finds out her feet will have begun to hurt. On the other hand, you don't want just one item; people will look at it without stopping and you'll lose the selling appeal of what may be some other sales-catching merchandise. There has been a test which alternated multiple-item and single-item displays in exactly the same location. The multiple-item display sold three times as much merchandise.

Put your merchandise up into the passer-by's line-of-sight and dress it up in an attention-commanding promotional setting. Another test found that the number of people who looked at promotional, up-where-you-could-see-them displays was twice the number who looked at displays which set their merchandise in the window's floor.

Arrange your merchandise so that it naturally leads the customer's eye from one item to the next.

Change the merchandise frequently. Otherwise your window will take on a comforting and familiar look to the passer-by and become a bit of scenery he passes and enjoys on his way to look in the windows of your competitors.

COLOR

Now you've got the merchandise in the window. Bare, isn't it? It looks like what the museum does with dinosaur eggs. That's because you're lacking the key tool in window display— color control.

Carefully controlled color can stop the passer-by cold, make him look at your window, then lead his eye to the items you want him to see and in the order you want him to see them. We've already seen that color is the key to eye appeal. Let's look at some color techniques that the color engineer uses to build this eye appeal in window display.

Simplicity

The window shopper is no art connoisseur in a gallery; on the contrary, she's somebody in a hurry. Complex color relationships and oversubtle colors will not delight her, and what's more, she won't stop to figure them out. Pure colors will catch her eye more readily than grayed ones; harmonious effects will draw her and discordant effects nudge her away.

Variety

Too much simplicity isn't good either. A single hue would be monotonous and unappealing. The answer is using well-placed accent colors with a total color impression of middle value—if values are too dark you get a dull and gloomy effect, if they're too light the window can look weak and anemic.

Light-Dark Balance

A window presentation gets its best chromatic balance through a strong light-dark contrast. A one-to-three ratio of light-to-dark value or strong-to-subdued chroma gives the best general balance.

Attention Getting

The attention getters are red, orange, and yellow. Purple-blue and purple are less effective; blue and blue-grays are attention-losing.

The trick in using attention-getting colors is balancing them with a much larger area of a neutral color. This will make the stopper color stand out. You can balance a spot of yellow with a large area of gray, for example (naturally, a spot of gray won't balance a large area of yellow).

Colorwise, the display man uses these attention-getting colors to lead the eye where you want it, but he must be careful that the accents don't compete. Two yellow spots would fight for the shopper's attention; if you want to lead his eye to objects in a one-two order, the first object would have to be set off with a yellow accent, the second with a blue one.

Harmony with the Merchandise

Since the merchandise in the window will have its own color,

66

REFLECTANCE

this is going to be one of the display engineer's prime considerations in his color choice. A neutral-colored item will tend to get lost against a bright, contrasting background. A strong-chroma item, on the other hand, requires a bright background to support and contrast with it. A royal blue bedspread shows up best against red or yellow; a pastel against darker gray or sand. Certain yellows make the most effective foil for the rainbow of apparel hues in the spring and summer season. Pastels —pink, salmon, light blue, turquoise—are good foils for bright intense colors. If it's food you're displaying in your window, red, green, golden brown, pink, and tan backgrounds will give the food colors their best eye appeal. Certain shades of medium-value purple make an attractive background for bread displays.

Color Combinations

The color and display engineer is always concerned with how colors act together. Here are some of the good combinations I've developed for window displays, and some of the poor ones I'm sorry to say I've seen.

GOOD COMBINATIONS:	POOR COMBINATIONS:
Blue and pink	Mustard and cardinal red
Green and sand	Blue and blue-green
Citron and dove gray	Chocolate and gun-metal gray
Brown and pink	Olive green and pink
Persimmon and white	Dark brown and emerald green
Yellow-green and olive green	

Who's the Customer?

In developing colors for window display, the color engineer considers carefully who is going to be looking in the window. Use feminine-looking colors for women's-store windows; for a men's window you want the strong masculine colors, and you should bear in mind that in-the-field tests show that men like blue best and red next. Women prefer red with blue a close second.

LIGHTING

One of the two biggest sources of selling power in the well-designed window display is the color of the merchandise and the way it is co-ordinated with its surroundings. The other is the window's illumination. Each type of merchandise you display has its own best-selling type of light source. What's the best source for the goods? The source which will make passers-by look at them.

Now let's look at the considerations which influence the color engineer when he prescribes the light for your show window.

Intensity

Can the shopper see? One department store found its sales dropping and traced the decline to a fall-off in window shopping. After considerable investigation it found the trouble across the street; a new front on an old building was reflecting light into the store's windows and washing out their lighting during the day. The store added more punch to its display lighting and sales went back up.

Intensity of light improves the speed and acuity of the shopper's vision and helps to counteract outside lighting like that reflection from the old building. Show windows in well-lighted areas sometimes need as much as 200 foot-candles of light to make them visible and to cut the effect of undesirable reflections in the glass.

Directional Control

Directional control eliminates glare, brings out textures and patterns, concentrates light for emphasis, and produces dramatically effective shadows.

We get directional lighting control by using mobile spotlights. The adjustable spotlight is an excellent tool for putting light where we want it; the new and comparatively inexpensive reflector-type bulbs serve very nicely as spots. When we use spotlighting, we generally keep light away from the background, using reflector floods or border lamps along the ceiling front to smooth out overspotted effects. Spotting at a 45-degree angle does the best job of bringing out plasticity of form in your merchandise. One of the dangers in this type of spotting, however, is that resultant shadows may fight with your merchandise for attention, a problem that a carefully engineered lighting layout can solve.

Diffusion

We diffuse light by a judicious use of reflectors and careful lighting placement. Diffusion eliminates undesirable shadows, raises the general lighting level in the window, and clarifies form.

Color Filtration

Light coming through a colored filter creates atmosphere, attracts attention, and emphasizes desirable undertones.

Colored lighting is one of the best ways we have for introducing color into the display window. We use it best as the old master used his glazes, to pull a display together and impart rich undertones to the merchandise colors. Light with a bluish cast gives a mink coat its greatest richness in appearance; amber- and straw-tinged lights do wonders for a creamy-white woolen blanket.

Colored light can give you remarkable effects. If two complementary colored lights bathe the same object it will stand out in clear white light and at the same time produce some fascinating colored shadows, one in each of the complementary colors. Such strong color techniques can attract attention to a piece of merchandise. Some of these color effects come from the phenomenon of color association that we've already discussed. A cool blue will make a Christmas display look more seasonal. Violet on a silver evening gown suggests glamour. Amber or orange filters used on your beachwear display evokes the warmth of summer.

The display engineer uses colored filters to color his light. Five basic filter colors will create as many as twelve useful light colors. The five basic filters are:yellow, green, blue, violet, red.

In combination these five can give us seven more:

COMBINATION	RESULTING LIGHT
Yellow and green	Lemon
Green and blue	Turquoise
Blue and violet	Indigo
Violet and red	Magenta
Red and blue	Scarlet
Red and yellow	Orange
Yellow and violet	Brown

One of the best ways you can put colored filters to work is with a device called the *Rainbo Mixer*. This consists of a spotlight shining through an aluminum frame containing two pairs of rollers, operating independently and at right angles to one another. Each pair carries a transparent plastic film in six colors (it adds amber to the basic filter list of five) plus a clear panel. Any color on the first roll can be superimposed on any color in the second. If you want only one color, you wind up one film until you reach its clear panel and put the desired color on the other.

The Rainbo Mixer (available through my firm, incidentally) is a versatile creature. It can give you two separate colors or the harlequin effect of four. It replaces the shelf-load of individual filters that you once had to keep on hand, and the color combinations from several Rainbo Mixers working in one window are almost limitless.

You can't use color indiscriminately in a window; that's one thing you have to bear in mind. Color can have some gloomy effects on your merchandise. Too intense color will create a theatrical effect. A blue light on red merchandise will make the red look muddy. Some reds will do sorry things to certain foods. It takes professional skill to pinpoint the regrettable effects that haphazard lighting can bring about.

FIXTURES, MATERIALS, AND PROPS

Fixtures have come a long way from those in the emporia

of our grandfathers. Mannequins have grown from the wax head, armless body, and skeleton skirt of the Victorian Era to today's plastic peacherinos straight out of the pages of *Vogue*. Wood has given way to a host of special-purpose plastics as the material for props. Papier-mâché abstractions replace the conventional display rack or shelf. Mobiles dangle from the ceiling. New types of window glass keep sunlight from draining the color in the display. Flameproof paper in a host of textures, colors, and patterns replaces textile drapery. Animated displays are looming larger, and picture-frame windows bring the technique of the stage into display.

The thing to remember in using all of these new aids is that they must enhance, not overshadow, the appearance of your merchandise. Color, lighting, fixtures, props—all must team together to make your windows unified, attractive, and sales-centered.

DISPLAY CARDS

The display window is an advertisement, a peculiarly economical and peculiarly effective one. Every advertisement has some text and your display window had better have some too. People want to know the price of your window's merchandise and where they will find it in the store. They want to know the size it comes in, and the terms for payment, if any. Text should be brief, clear, and to the point. It is the special concern of the display manager that text should be equally legible and distinctive.

Most text in your window gets there by way of display cards. Too often these cards are undersized, hard to read, and not co-ordinated. Too often, also, they have opposite faults: they are so big, blatant, and bunched together that a looker can't see the merchandise for cards. Display cards must serve as auxiliary salesmen. They should not compete with the merchandise they talk about. Yet they must not be so innocuous that the shopper will have to press his nose against the glass to find out where they are.

Here are some of the important things you should know about display cards.

They must be visible and therefore attention-getting. Black on yellow is out and away the best color combination for legibility. Red on white and blue on white come next, and there are many other good combinations. No matter which you use, passers-by will develop an effective immunity to any you use too often.

They must be legible. You should be able to read a display card easily at least ten feet away. This means at least 48-point type and a readable type face; florid scripts or other fancy type faces don't work. Keep your type style in keeping with the nature of the display. High-fashion clothes styles call for modern type faces like Futura or Lydian, while a window full of hearty foods, on the other hand, could well profit from strong and more old-fashioned type fonts like Bodoni or Cheltenham.

They must be distinctive. Can you move one of your display cards, exhibit it away from your store, and still identify your store by the card's special characteristics? If you can't, you need professional color and design guidance.

They must be informative. You can come up with a veritable masterpiece of display-card design and still find it doesn't do you any good because the card didn't say anything in the first place. Spend as much time on the copy and layout of your cards as you do on your ads. No matter what the display engineer tries to do for you, he can't help you if you have worded your card badly.

They must be current. If you leave the old display cards in the window—especially manufacturer's display cards—you're losing the here-and-now appeal of up-to-the-minute promotion. Keep your display cards geared to the seasons, to fashion trends, to current events, to anything that will make your window something new. An old display is like yesterday's newspaper. The passer-by has already read it and it's not likely that he's going to bother to do so again.

COLOR: SUPERSALESMAN FOR YOUR PACKAGE

Unless you are selling live goats or battleships, the odds are very good that your product greets its prospective buyer in some sort of package. This package is your ultimate salesman. It takes over where your advertising and promotion and sales force leave off. It is your last chance to influence the customer before the sale, and no matter how well you've softened up that customer and made him want your product, your package—its appearance and effect and use—is either going to clinch that sale or lose it. You may be spending thousands of dollars now on your packaging and putting a platoon of dud salesmen on the firing line. Without spending a penny more, you may be able to give those salesmen some firepower. The key? Color and design. In this chapter we're going to look at some of the ways that careful color and design planning can help make a supersalesman out of your package.

PACKAGE COLOR: WHAT IT DOES AND HOW IT WORKS

There is a survey by the Du Pont Company which shows that

78 per cent of supermarket purchases are unplanned. A package caught the customer's eye, then recalled a need or created a desire. Quite a feat, considering that a supermarket, today, may display as many as six thousand different items. The A. & P. chain, for example, does an annual business of $4.5 billion. Surveys show that the average shopper spends $4.80 per supermarket visit. Therefore, in this chain alone, a manufacturer's product and package is on display before a total audience of almost a billion shoppers.

In drug stores 53 per cent of buying was found to be on impulse—much of this impelled by packaging and display. Point-of-sale impact generated 38 per cent of candy sales. In all of this impulse buying, color played the dominant role.

Color works eight ways in helping your package become a salesman:

1. It commands attention.
2. It portrays your product.
3. It builds and maintains brand identification.
4. It adds eye interest.
5. It convinces the customer that the product will perform its function: that party napkins will be cheerful, for example, or an after-shave lotion cool.
6. It creates impulse sales.
7. It moves merchandise faster.
8. It never contradicts the desired impression.

Color cannot do these jobs alone. Design, display, store background, and lighting will all affect your package's selling success. But with these factors constant, the proper use of color will move your product faster and make more dollars for you. No matter how well a package is designed, promoted and merchandised, if presented in the wrong color schemes, it will not reach its full sales potential. Witness three examples:

Back before the war, a British firm was slugging it out with a United States company in selling near-identical packaged products, at the same price, in South America. Gradually, the British company fell behind until the U.S. firm led in sales, ten-to-one. The English package was predominantly black. It failed to appeal to the colorful Latin temperament. The U.S. package, with red predominating, had stolen the market.

Holsum Bread, a big supermarket seller, found its sales soaring when it adopted a new wrapper in orange-red, a warm and "edible" color.

The Minnesota Valley Canning Company capitalized on the fresh, appetizing nature of its canned foods by adopting a Green Giant trademark. The Leo Burnett Agency of Chicago convinced Minnesota Valley to put the Giant and his food-related color to work. He grew larger and found jobs to do on ads and packages. The Green Giant became such a successful salesman that the company even took his name for its own.

If the foregoing examples have had their effect, you should be wondering about your own packaging. A change in package design and color should be instituted under the most advantageous economic and competitive circumstances. I have found that clients benefit most if they make a change when: (1) package inventory is low; (2) new printing plates are needed; (3) sales show a decrease; (4) the present package does not make an effective showing in newspaper, TV, and magazine advertisements.

A strategic package-color change can give a container a decided jump on competitors.

WHAT PACKAGE COLOR SHOULD YOU USE?

There are several considerations which help the professional color engineer decide which colors to employ on which packages. First, there are the color associations we've discussed in some of our previous chapters. These color associations and their effects can be a subtle business; sometimes minor differences, even in the same general hue, can make a big impact difference. Let's look at some of these color effects.

75

Although in a general way colors may be said to invoke certain moods, it must always be remembered that these are apt to vary with the individual. Childhood associations of certain colors with pleasure or pain are apt to persist through life. Nor can color be completely dissociated from the object that it embellishes. For example, a woman wearing an emerald green evening gown may well feel elated and gay in it, but in a room with walls of the same shade she would be apt to be driven into a state of violent depression.

So far as generalizations can be made about the moods induced by color, the following associations are valid. Note that different values and intensities of the same color very often have quite opposite connotations.

Light reds induce cheerfulness, but *very dark* or *very bright reds* are more likely to induce depression and irritability.

Soft pinks are associated with femininity but *bright magenta pinks* suggest frivolity.

Light orange looks clean and appetizing but *when this color is grayed to a tan shade,* it merely looks drab.

Pale yellow and *ivory* suggest daintiness, but *deep, strong yellow* is a sensuous color, suggesting near and tangible things.

A clear, fairly light yellow-green is associated with young growth and freshness, but *the same color darkened and subdued to olive* brings to mind a feeling of decay.

Light sky blue is a tranquil color; *deepened to indigo,* it becomes depressing.

Light violet-blue induces restfulness and serenity; *deep violet-blue* suggests depth and distance.

Pale lavender is feminine, but *insipid, deep purple* becomes oppressive and productive of melancholia.

The applications of these color effects to packaging are easy to imagine. It would be a color-foolish manufacturer indeed who swathed his screwdriver in the delicacy of pink or packaged his New Year's Eve noisemaker in the calmness of drab gray.

76

These psychological considerations can have some other obvious effects. Frozen-food manufacturers, for example, have
capitalized on color psychology; their sales climbed when they
abandoned the blue and green cool colors of prewar days and
packaged their foods in warm and appetizing colors coupled
with illustrations showing the food ready for eating.

The effectiveness of modern package-color techniques was
recently underscored by Dr. James G. Miller, director of the
University of Michigan's Mental Health Institute; he mentioned the case of a woman who fortified herself with tran-
quilizers before every visit to J. L. Hudson's Department Store
in Detroit—so she would have less difficulty resisting the
impulse to buy the excitingly colored packages and other merchandise.

The visual mechanics of color—another topic we've met
before—also have a big influence on the colors for your package. If we ignore these mechanics we may wind up with a
package which will produce the psychological reaction we want
once the consumer's eye has found it—but which may not
catch the consumer's eye in the first place. This raises the
more complex problem of combining colors—not a package in
a thousand is a one-color job.

Certain colors increase a package's visibility: black on a
certain yellow, and a special green on white, for example. A
small area of a discordant color can work equally well to make
your package more attention-getting. A small patch of pale
purple on a red and orange package is one example; so is a dab
of crimson on blue-green.

But in designating color for packages and products, there are
many pitfalls avoided by the color-wise. Recently, a friend of
mine, who had spent some hours in his local supermarket, came
into my office bursting with the news that not one of the
thousands of items on display was packaged in white. Therefore, he concluded, white would be a terrific attention-getter
on the shelves. I agreed, but pointed out that the white package
would probably be so discolored and spoiled by handling,

77

before it even reached the buyer, that it would undoubtedly prove unsalable.

Different package color plans will vary in basic harmony and eye appeal. Here is a list of some of those color plans that shows how they stack up against each other.

SOME GOOD COLOR COMBINATIONS
Scarlet and Turquoise
Scarlet and Royal Blue
Periwinkle Blue and Deep Violet
Vermilion and Purple
Vermilion and Bright Navy Blue
Magenta and Light Turquoise
Light Peach and Dark Violet
Orange and Dark Blue
Lemon Yellow and Bark Brown
Chartreuse and Violet
Pearl Gray and Bright Vermilion
Chartreuse and Coral Pink
Lime Yellow and Medium Blue
Turquoise and Violet

SOME POOR COLOR COMBINATIONS
Scarlet and Green
Scarlet and Yellow
Scarlet and Violet
Orange and Purple
Yellow and Bright Red
Tan and Crimson
Bright Pink and Orange
Olive and Blue
Beige and Light Gray
Charcoal and Brown
Charcoal and Purple
Pink and Orange
Green and Purple
Turquoise and Yellow Green

SOME FAIR COLOR COMBINATIONS
Orange and Green
Orange-Yellow and Purple
Orange-Yellow and Turquoise
Yellow and Green
Lime Yellow and Purple
Green and Vermilion
Turquoise and Blue

PROVIDED THE RIGHT VARIATIONS
OF LIGHTNESS AND COLOR
STRENGTH ARE USED
Lime Yellow and Turquoise
Turquoise and Green

COLOR AND LEGIBILITY

You may have a high-priced writer on your staff grinding out snappy sales copy for the omnivorous reader of package-back prose, but you're not getting your money's worth unless customers can read what your man has to say. One is tempted to say that this is self-evident, but as I write this there repose upon my desk three packages, one lettered in white on a pale yellow background, another lettered in maroon on a dark blue background, and the third featuring white lettering against a pale pink ground. I can't read these packages from four feet away, and I doubt that any prospective customer will bother to read them at all.

You are by now growing familiar with some of the mechanics of color harmony and contrast. These are the laws which determine the legibility of package text, and here are some specific applications of the laws to the problem of keeping your package's lettering legible.

Any lettering on a colored background is heightened by outlining the letters in gold, silver, white, or black; of course, each of these is not equally effective on every background. In general, the color relationship embodying the greatest contrast is desirable.

Colored lettering on a background in a complementary color, if the colors are dark, stands out more clearly when outlined in a lighter value of the background color (for example, red on green outlined in a lighter shade of green). If both the colors are light in value, outline the lettering in a darker value of the package color.

Colored lettering on a white or black background is legible without outlining if the lettering color is not too high in value (too light) on the white background, or too low in value (too dark) on the black background for effective contrast.

The nearer in value (lightness or darkness) and in purity the lettering color is to the background color, the wider and more pronounced the dark outline for the lettering should be.

Dark-color lettering on a background of contrasting dark color requires an outline in a light variation of either color.

Colored lettering on a bright, light color should be outlined in a darker value of the lettering color (for example, green lettering on gold should be outlined in a darker green).

Gold lettering on any background stands out effectively with an edging in black.

79

THE THIRTEEN KEYS TO PACKAGE COLOR

We have seen some of the ways in which correct color can put your package on the sales force. Now let's draw from these specific color applications and formulate thirteen general rules for using color to stimulate the selling appeal of your package.

1. *Use a color plan that will attract attention.* This is vital with today's increasing emphasis on impulse buying and with the increasing visual competition from the décor in stores.

2. *Emphasize your product's quality through its package.* If it's an expensive product, make it look expensive; if it's a cheap, mass-distribution item, don't clothe it in the colors of high fashion.

3. *Emphasize any special features of the product through color;* a good example is the use of green on packages for products containing chlorophyll. If your product is a time-saver, its color plan should suggest quickness; if its advantage is durability, it should try for a feeling of substance through the use of robust-looking maroons or browns; if the product's colors themselves best serve your sales needs, transparent packaging is often the answer. One caution here: be sure that whoever develops your transparent package understands that many transparent substances can throw a distorting color cast on their contents.

4. *Make food packages look clean and appetizing.*

5. *Point up the important parts of the package and subordinate its less important areas.* Dominant, advancing colors should be used in the areas of a package which you want the customer to see first; receding colors will play down features of secondary importance.

6. *Build a family resemblance into the packaging of related products in your line.* This stimulates sales of the related products and helps the retailer set up his shelves. It gives the display of your products a unified selling punch that unrelated packages are hard put to achieve.

7. *Keep directions and instructions in a color which contrasts*

sharply with the other color or colors on your package. This will make for legibility and therefore for fast and easy comprehension. The package should catch the customer's eye when he is at least seven feet away; its lettering should be readily legible at arm's length.

8. *Use as little copy as possible.* The more your package depends on color imagery, design, and symbols to get its sales message across, the more effective it will be. Lettering should only confirm and amplify what your package's color plan tells.

9. *Use only bright, warm colors on frozen-food products.* There are two reasons for this. First, these are the colors with the best food associations. Second, these are the colors which best show through the package's normal layer of frost.

10. *Make the price visible;* the self-service customer is eminently price-conscious. The best way to do this is by providing an adequate white space on the package for price-marking. If the price is indeed visible it will prevent unnecessary handling by the customer, an important consideration in self-service selling. The placement of price-marking space is also a convenience feature important to market and store operators.

11. *Use pictures if you cannot let the customer see your product itself.* Halftones from modern color photos show your customer what he can expect. An ingenious package incorporating this technique is the Crackerjack box adopted in the fall of 1956—it does a handsome job of combining the technical advantages of foil wrapping with the sales advantages of color picture printing.

12. *Design your package with prevalent store lighting in mind.* Some types of lighting distort certain colors; they can blunt the impact of a good color plan for your package. Before developing your package's colors, test them under different types of lighting and actual store conditions. This insures that their intended effect is not lost.

13. *Pretest your package.* If you tool up for a new package without getting consumer reaction, you are playing blindman's buff with your budget. One of the color engineer's most im-

portant tools in package design and planning is the survey he uses to find out if a planned package will really sell in practice.

PACKAGE COLOR AND DESIGN

As we've already seen in examining many of the other business and industrial applications of color, color and design work together—as popular idiom has it, you can't have one without the other.

Here are some of the design problems the color engineer will have to face in his work on your package.

Is it easy to open? Wrapped boxes generally aren't. Ray Eisenhardt, the package construction wizard, advocates a thin, built-in nylon rip-cord which will cut both cardboard and paper wrapping, yet leave the package easy to close. Color can highlight this rip-cord or whatever other easy-opening device you use; it can lead the customer's eye to the device and make its operation easy to understand.

Does it stack easily? The old Simonize can with the spout at the side didn't; it required a costly paper collar for each unit. The new can wears its spout at the top, fitting into a dent in the bottom of the next can up in the stack. Stacked products lend themselves aptly to adroit color planning; a well-designed stack with a carefully thought-out color plan can accumulate considerable extra visual impact.

Is it sturdy? Self-service selling subjects the package to an enormous amount of man- and woman-handling. Color, of course, can help point up the fact that your package is indeed sturdy, a strong consideration for the housewife who is loath to deposit a trail of flour, green peas, or vitamin pills between the store and her home.

Is the package convenient to handle? Here again color can emphasize its convenience.

Does the package feel good in the hand? The whole appeal to tactile sense looms large with the growth of self-service buying. This calls for smooth surfaces, rounded edges, and simple shapes; color will dramatize these features once you build them in.

Is your package two-faced? It had better be, or else its color plan may wind up trying to sell the package to the supermarket wall.

Can you profit by unit packaging? Many manufacturers find that the tie-in package—razor, razor blades, and shaving cream, packed together, for example—is a strong sales builder. Color can bring unity to the tie-in package, as well as through the entire line.

Thus, color in family packaging enhances the relating of different packages in a manufacturer's line by carrying a unified theme of color through the entire line.

It does four jobs: It stimulates the sales of related products; it helps the retailer to set up his shelves; it adds visual impact to displays of products; and it capitalizes on color associations the manuafcturer may have already built up—on the colors, logotype, trucks, letterhead and the like.

THE TAG: COUSIN TO THE PACKAGE

Tag it well and it will sell!

Back at the beginning of the chapter we said that most of today's products are packaged. If they're not, the odds are overwhelming that dangling from them someplace is the package's cousin, the tag. Tags and packages replace sales clerks in the modern market; such diverse articles as clothes, refrigerators, and even small animals currently are being sold self-service.

The rules we laid down for the package apply equally well to the tag. Tag colors must be appropriate to the product and must stimulate interest in it; the colors must be effective under all types of illumination. Tags must contrast with the merchandise they talk about, they must be legible, and they must be eye-catching. They should be printed on a stock which will readily take the price imprint, and they had better be durable—

83

24 per cent of the self-selection tags examined in a study of women's ready-to-wear worked their way off their garments before final sale.

Current tag colors and designs are cut-and-dried and fearfully lackluster. They fail to exploit the powerful punch of color in moving merchandise. Often, the colors used are outrageous. One of the color engineer's special fields of effort is creating tags which will carry out the visual effectiveness of their merchandise and thereby help, not hinder, the self-selection sale.

For example, in furniture stores or furniture departments, tagged furniture outsold the untagged by a ratio of 7 to 1; rugs and carpets, 3 to 1; electrical toasters, 8 to 1; portable radios, 5 to 1; lamps 3.5 to 1.

A study which covered seventy-two cities in a variety of stores said that "although tags are a powerful and indispensable aid at the point of sale, it does not mean that any tag will do." There is a right and wrong tag. *Yellow, for example, is an effective color for selling certain items, whi'e blue or red are better for others.* Large tags should be used on freezers and refrigerators, rather than small ones. The study proved that:

> Customers take time to read informative tags.
>
> Proper tagging permits quicker turnover.
>
> People want more information than is contained on the average package today.
>
> Less merchandise is returned because of fuller information on the tag.
>
> Consumers are educated to look for tags.
>
> Shoppers will buy more tagged articles because tags supply the budget-stretching information they are looking for today.

The right colors on your tag or package do wonderful things at extremely low cost. Color improves the appearance of quality. It adds gay, festive effects for special promotions. It can be traditional.

Above all, avoid a color that looks so general that it might be used by any company. There are more than ten million colors from which to choose.

Unfortunately, today's mass-production techniques in the packaging industry are also being applied to the design and color planning of the package. One has only to examine the various packages of cake mixes on the market and then review cake mix advertising to note the visual confusion and lack of individuality in both package and advertising color art.

In today's competitive supermarkets, featuring well over six thousand items, the hackneyed, passive, trite color scheme doesn't have a chance of coping with consumer resistance.

PACKAGES AROUND PACKAGES: CARTONS

In appearance, today, the average shipping carton is a dirty-looking, brown box printed with ugly type in black ink—designed to be thrown away. But, in terms of tomorrow, the neglected, unattractive shipping carton promises to provide manufacturers and stores with a virtually untapped, highly effective, and colorful display and advertising medium.

Shipping cartons are beginning to come out of the shadows and into the bright lights of the high-traffic aisles in "bare-bones" retail outlets. Cartons are being used to display merchandise in the mushrooming supermarkets, drug chains, variety stores, filling stations, and low-price retail outlets which account for more than 60 per cent of grocery, drug, appliance, and hardware sales. Cartons, like packages, must be color-designed for maximum selling effectiveness.

In the impulse world of "bare-bones" merchandising, a carton is often *the* package, *the* ultimate point-of-purchase seller—the only "salesman" the manufacturer has.

A linear foot of advertising space in self-service stores is now worth approximately $150. Yet, lining the high-traffic areas of most "bare-bones" stores are thousands of nondescript cartons, often with blank sides several square feet in area. These large, empty areas of brown cardboard can, however, be used as sales adjuncts for your packages. The space is yours—free of charge. Both the manufacturer and the store will profit from its use.

Market-research tests have proved that skillfully designed cartons used for display increase sales in self-service hardware stores by 50 per cent, in self-service drugstores by 150 per cent. We also know that the cost of such attention-getting cartons is nominal compared with their effectiveness for sales and advertising. These surveys emphasize the fact that cartons are the most efficient, least expensive, unexploited advertising and selling medium.

Here are some typical, basic carton-design features which my company has found to be effective.

The primary function of the carton is to impart optimum sales impact at the point of purchase and while it is in transit.

1. The only sure, quick, direct way to attract attention from across a store is with carefully created, thoroughly researched, color design.

2. This color design must not be dulled by the natural brown of the carton but should contrast legibly with it.

3. Colors must be appealing and clearly noticeable under modern store lighting.

4. The carton, like the package, must have, build, and maintain color identification—for quick brand recognition, consumer appeal, and repeat sales. Table products, for example, must be in cartons that suggest cleanliness, hardware in cartons that suggest durability.

5. During loading or unloading, at freight depots or in similar situations where his cartons are in public view, the manufacturer reaps a display and brand-identification bonus.

The design, including color, brand name, trade-mark, etc., must be kept simple.

1. Our research shows that one striking over-all design, or a

"step-and-repeat" design, is best; in general, no more than two colors should be used.

2. The carton must be "two-faced" or, preferably, "four-faced." Remember, you don't know which side of the carton will be showing, or how much of it.

3. We recommend that all copy be simple, relaying the basic, sales-getting information. Space should be left where promotions, product changes or special offers can be announced.

4. Type faces must be big, easy to read from a distance, and appropriate to the character of the product. A type face such as Airport black is good for hardware; Caslon for food-product neatness; Eve for feminine identification; and Venus Bold Extended for gasoline pump lettering.

Naturally, the carton must be a good box: sturdy, inexpensive, convenient to handle, stack and display. It must be easy to open and to use as a display bin. More elaborate cartons can have special pop-up tops, inside-of-lid advertising, or top-panel display inserts.

Cartons, like packages, are now being designed to advertise, attract attention, identify, and "color sell." Manufacturers can take immense advantage of the large sales potential of successfully designed cartons. "Bare-bones" merchandising can be a blessing to those who have taken advantage of modern color design and sell from cartons having a strong visual appeal.

COLOR AND LIGHT IN THE FACTORY

Amos Alonzo Stagg, the great football coach, understood the psychological power of color. He had his team's dressing room painted a relaxing blue to calm and rest the players during the half-time period, but he used an exciting, brilliant red anteroom for last-minute pep talks. Another coach, the fiercely competitive Knute Rockne, used a different approach. He kept his players stimulated throughout their half-time break with a red-walled dressing room, while he attempted to lull visiting teams with restful blue in their quarters. Both coaches were taking advantage of a fact that many industries are now applying to their profit: color has a great influence on how people act.

So far in this book we have seen color in action as a sales tool. Now we're going to examine a different application of color—color increasing worker efficiency in industry. Today the proper use of color has become vitally important in industrial planning and plant design.

Ask a shipping clerk to move one of two differently colored shipping crates of equal size—one painted pale blue and the other painted dark brown. He will unhesitatingly start for the

88

blue crate. Why? Because the pale blue color gives the impression that it is lighter in weight. Tell the clerk to move the crate to either of two tables—one red and one blue—each twenty feet distant, and he will move it to the red one. Why? Because the red table seems to be at least a full step closer.

A service acquaintance tells me that the U.S. Army has cautioned its drivers to park carefully in a space that happens to be between two blue cars. Why? Because such a space gives the impression that it is wider than it is.

We see in these examples that color has a subtle but positive impact on the mind. Color's psychological effect is becoming more widely recognized as part of sound industrial planning. This effect is part of our everyday experience, like the air we breathe, but only recently has scientific research systematized our knowledge of the subject so that today we can make full use of the complex impact which color has on our welfare. Consciously or unconsciously, color exerts a constant influence on us all, and it is an established fact that color contributes immeasurably to our emotional well-being. Color can create the effect of warmth or coldness, of advancing toward or receding from the eye. It can be bright or depressing, pleasing or irritating, refined or crude, exciting or relaxing. And such effects are important in work areas.

No matter where people work, whether in a large factory or a small area, color (and its constant companion, lighting) will affect their jobs. Over thirty years of sound and practical research have proved that skillfully selected colors create better and more comfortable working and seeing conditions, raise efficiency, cut fatigue, and increase production. More and more, astute management is realizing that when there is painting to be done, it is profitable to do it right with functional color.

If paint for the interior of a large factory costs approximately $50,000, the time and labor entailed in apply that paint costs approximately $150,000 more. In the light of this expense, it stands to reason that intelligent guidance, by a qualified specialist in color, in the selection and application of paint colors is an investment well worth making. The benefits of the functional use of color are at once apparent and positive for both employer and employee. Here are some of the positive results from the use of correct color: better morale, greater safety, more efficiency and less waste, reduction of nervous tension and eyestrain, better workmanship, higher output, less absenteeism, fewer accidents, and better labor-management relations.

Intelligent use of color and lighting in factories is daily reducing fatigue, providing visibility necessary to accurate and accident-free operation, and getting rid of confusion, waste, lost motion, and actual damage caused by unintentional camouflage of hazards and danger areas.

CASE HISTORIES

The emotional lift that proper color gives to workers can be striking. For example, a radio-tube manufacturer encountered a problem on his production line. An important operation involved high-precision welding by women using machines with gas jets placed in a circle; he found that this hot and exacting work tired the women and strained their eyes. Color planning came to the rescue. Work benches painted sky blue (a psychologically cool color) counterbalanced the heat from the welding. The machines themselves were painted light orange for contrast with the dark gas jets. Dark blue directly under the machines heightened the visibility of the bright metal machine parts. Most of this manufacturer's employees had previously been aware of nothing but drab, colorless interiors. The new color arrangement was, therefore, extraordinarily well received. The operators in all sections began to clamor for similar color plans. Foremen became so enthusiastic that they did a lot of repainting themselves. Some employees bought denim dusters in colors to match their machines! The plant became markedly cleaner. Most important of all, shrinkage—that is rejects, breakage, anything not passing inspection—showed an immediate and marked decrease. Rejects on one item decreased two-thirds

90

within the first week, Every cent that manufacturer expended on paint was more than repaid and morale was materially boosted.

Another case history:

Not long ago, the Wire and Rope Division of the Jones and Laughlin Steel Corporation completed a color-engineering project. Working time lost through accidents *dropped 38 per cent* in the first six months after the job was finished. The improved employee morale reduced absenteeism from about 5 per cent to less than 2 per cent. Labor turnover dropped astoundingly. Operator efficiency on complicated wire-twisting equipment climbed from 85 to 90 per cent from the time the color project was started until it was completed.

A third case:

After functional color planning was instituted at the Portsmouth Rod and Wire Division of the Detroit Steel Company, at Portsmouth, Ohio, a report stated:

When we adopted the functional color plan . . . our accident-frequency rate stood at 9.2. Our records . . . show that this figure has been reduced to 2.3—*a drop of 75%*. And the severity of these accidents has substantially fallen from .90 to .37. Our workers are certainly appreciative of the pleasant working conditions that have been accomplished, and we have noticed that our employees take more pride in their work which reflects considerably in the quality and quantity of production.

A fourth case:

In a New York precision-tool plant, after color was properly co-ordinated on machinery and walls, absenteeism was cut by 60 per cent, rejects were reduced by 40 per cent, and the production rate was raised 15 per cent!

A fifth case:

In a Brockton, Massachusetts, factory, shoemakers had worked at black machines, using black thread, stitching black shoes. The wall colors had been equally gloomy and dismal. Light-green, blue, orange, and cream paint colors brought more light and freshness to their work areas and surroundings. Particular

91

attention was given to background and to attention-compelling background colors, such as orange, to help direct special attention to moving parts. Workers soon reported less eyestrain and there was relief from nervous fatigue; in consequence, absenteeism declined. Best of all, the accident rate fell off sharply with the introduction of functional color. Here is the way one worker expressed himself:

I didn't realize what was causing me to feel my age until these machines were painted. My eyes were bothering me and I had to get glasses long ago. When I got home nights I'd have a general nervous and tired feeling, and I got so I couldn't throw it off with a night's sleep. When those machines were painted a light color I noticed my eyes weren't bothering me as they were before. The work is easier to see and the whole place is brighter and cleaner. I felt better right away.

The president of that Brockton shoe company also had a high opinion about the usefulness of color:

Color has been such a boon we buy paint just as we do machinery. We can't do without it. White walls and ceilings to give us the most light, blues, greens, oranges, creams, buffs, etc., on the machinery to give us the cheer and scientific contrast we need, mean better workmen, better plants, better production and, of course, more profit. Shoes are inspected closer and rejections are fewer. We feel the beneficial results even in our sales force working through the country. We've cut down the number of accidents. Do our employees like it? Over 65% of them bought paint to redecorate interiors and exteriors of their homes within a year after we allowed them to color the plant.

FATIGUE AND CONTRAST

In virtually every type of factory and industry, a worker is using his eyes constantly. The mechanics of seeing are closely connected to fatigue. When the worker is exposed continuously to only one color, however pleasant it may be, he is using nerve endings in only one part of his eye for color perception. This concentrated effort of one set of nerve endings can result in early fatigue. Thus, there is a distinct need for *color variation* to help avoid fatigue among factory workers.

Another factor which causes worker fatigue is color contrast. If, through lack of planning, a desk worker is found to be working with white paper on a dark desk-top surface, he will contantly be seeing strong contrasts. In terms of the eye, this means a constant opening and closing of the pupil. The excessive mucular movement within the eye contributes to fatigue. So, a practical color plan for a desk work surface, for example, must effect minimal contrasts between paper and desk top. A medium-gray desk top will answer this need.

Anyone who has tried to thread a needle will appreciate why mill workers looping thread over a series of fine needles are tired by strong light contrasts and distracted by the movement of neighboring workers. Gray-blue panels around the work tables shut out all confusion and provide the needed neutral eye-resting background. A small gray mask behind a riveting machine, pin-pointing the operator's attention and cutting fatigue and visual distraction, can cut down on contrast-bred faulty estimates of distance and thus save many fingers from damage.

We find another example of the harmful effects of excessive color contrast in the factory in the full-fashioned hosiery industry. So exacting is the work that at one time the average useful life of the eyes of a worker was only about ten years. The Ajax Hosiery Mills studied this problem in an attempt to lengthen this useful span and make hosiery work less of a strain. Ajax found that color was the answer. At the time the study started, complete stockings were being placed on shiny white tables for visual inspection before packing. It was thought that white afforded the best contrast to the dark stockings. But the study showed that gazing at the glossy white surface eight hours a day was measurably tiring. Ajax refinished its inspection tables in a dull-finish light pastel blue. The new color minimized glare, relieved eyestrain, and proved a big boon to Ajax's workers. Ajax painted its menders' tables, too, using a light blue on the working surface and a pastel green along the edges. The result was not only an attractive table but one which once again cut down harmful and tiring glare and contrast.

The Bethlehem Steel Corporation, in an issue of its company bulletin, *Bethlehem Review,* has this to say on color's contribution to its activities:

All Bethlehem operations have long used color for identification and safety purposes. Pipes and mains have been coded by color, and fire-fighting apparatus and special safety equipment have been painted to increase their efficiency through prompt use without mistakes. It is difficult, for example, not to associate red with either fire or danger. In the same way, Bethlehem employees have come to know that safety lanes or aisles are marked with white or yellow.

Color has also long been used for purposes of shipping and inventory control. Through association, customers and dealers have come to recognize certain colors as part of the Bethlehem advertising program. . . . In recent years, color has played an additional part in industrial operations. It has been used to enhance artificial illumination and to reduce eye fatigue. Distinctive coloring in the plant is finding many new industrial applications. . . . This type of painting may be more fully described as the use of scientific color schemes for machinery and shop interiors, walls, floors and ceilings, in a correct combination with natural and artificial light to make it easier for the employee to see his work with a minimum of distraction and to provide a maximum of safety and efficiency.

For example, a machine is painted a color which will reflect light rather than absorb it, thus increasing the usable light at the point where it is needed most. Moving parts and controls are painted a contrasting, scientifically-chosen color, which enables the operator to more readily identify the controls and to avoid possible injury from fumbling. The background of the working area, such as walls, floors and ceilings, is painted a "spotlight" color which highlights the machine, reduces blinding glares, and relieves eyestrain by increasing visibility to the maximum.

Such color application must always be the result of accurate study and appraisal. . . . The use of color in this way differs somewhat from ordinary painting in that it takes into account the human or psychoglogical factor as well as physical elements. Morale improves in correctly illuminated and painted interiors, even as the chance of accident decreases and production consequently increases.

Color has been applied with marked success by large oil

companies in their refineries. At three Esso Standard plants —
Bayonne and Bayway, in New Jersey, and Baton Rouge, Louisiana—painting programs were found to have both aesthetic and
practical values. Distinctive colors were used to designate the
special equipment, and variegated colors designated what
fluids were flowing through particular pipes. Bright colors
warned of potentional danger spots and pale reflective colors
aided visibility in dark areas. This is especially helpful to night
workers. At these plants, the workers were permitted to select
the colors they wanted to work with, which proved to be a
morale boost. At the Louisiana refinery the color program comprised nineteen different but harmonious hues chosen to meet
the personal taste of the operators. Esso officials found the new
colors made the refineries cleaner and improved maintenance.

Read what Mr. D. F. Edwards, General Superintendent of
Esso's Bayonne Refinery, had to say about the color program's
effects:

The color program in Bayonne is a success. It has stimulated
employee interest and pride in their immediate work areas and in
the refinery as a whole. In the past three years we have carried out an
ambitious program of rehabilitation in our offices, cafeteria, wash
and locker rooms and shops. New and clean surroundings always
stimulate morale and improve housekeeping. The color program has
been used to increase employee interest and esprit de corps through
participation.

When planning the renovation of an office or shop, we have made
a practice of consulting the people working in the area. We ask them
to choose color schemes and make other suggestions. The end result
is arrived at by group participation. There is no doubt that the use
of color makes our surroundings more attractive and comfortable.
We also feel we have obtained a tremendous amount of employee
satisfaction and a feeling of participation, of "being on the team."

The Phillips Petroleum Company also has dressed up its
plants considerably with focal-point painting, making them
more attractive as well as more utilitarian. An oil refinery is no
thing of beauty on the industrial scene, but the management
realized that brightening the plants created much good will in

95

the community and increased the workers' pride in their company. The Phillips refinery personnel wanted to maintain identification with the company's service stations, so the Phillips sales colors were successfully used in the painting program of the refinery.

PROFIT FROM MAKING
YOUR EMPLOYEES HAPPIER

Still another instance of the investment return on money spent for color engineering is the New Philadelphia, Ohio, plant of Warner & Swasey, whose vice-president in charge of manufacturing, Myron Curtis, stated:

We chose to use color functionally in order to create an environment that would be pleasing, cheerful and, at the same time, improve the productivity of our operators. We selected colors that would increase visibility without causing eye fatigue.

We also painted recreation and rest areas in colors that would provide a welcome change of pace and return the workers to their jobs feeling alert and refreshed. Above all, we wanted to create a work place of which the entire community could be proud. How well we succeeded is best shown by the enthusiastic comments when we held "open house" at the time of our opening. This was further confirmed by the flood of applications from men who wanted to work in these surroundings.

The plant engineer of the H. J. Heinz Company had this to say about color in his plant cafeterias:

One cafeteria is for the plant men, one for the plant women and one for both the male and female members of the general office force. All the cafeterias were colored differently, the first two with a warmer feeling than the last. The lower part of that one's walls are a dark blue tile with a motif that represents a sea wave. Blue is cool; water is cool. The walls are buff, with a little admixture of blue in their surfacing. One winter a lot of the girls complained about the temperature of their cafeteria, saying it was too cold. We have all three under thermostatic control; there were no complaints from the others, and on checking I found plenty of heat in all of them.

96

So we decided to heat the place with color. We put orange slip covers on the backs of all the chairs and an orange-and-black decorative band around the walls at about the height of the molding. You could take one look at this previously cool room and see warmth all over it. The complaints stopped almost immediately.

COLOR IN SCHOOLS

Scholastic achievement and behavior of pupils improve markedly when pleasing color is introduced in schoolrooms, a recent study proves. The improvement was especially striking among kindergarten children, whose performance rose by more than a third as a result of scientific color application.

The experiment was conducted by a group of educators and psychologists in three schools that needed repainting. One of these was left unpainted. Another was refinished in conventional colors, light buff walls and white ceilings. The third was painted in accordance with modern principles of color dynamics: Corridor walls were given cheerful yellow color, with gray doors and map boards. Classrooms with northern exposure were painted pale rose while those facing south were finished in cool shades of blue and green. Art classrooms alone were painted neutral light gray, so that the décor would not interfere with the colorful work produced there. Front walls of classrooms were painted a darker shade of the prevailing wall color.

Green chalkboards were used to reduce glare and to minimize the contrast with the surrounding wall.

Over a two-year test period, the pupils in the "psychologically" painted school showed the greatest improvement in each of seven performance traits studied. Those in the unpainted school showed the least. The traits studied were social habits, health and safety habits, work habits, language arts, arithmetic, social studies and science, art and music. So, here too, properly resolved color planning pays worth-while dividends in work performance.

97

BRITAIN KNOWS THE COLOR SCORE

Some of the most extensive uses of functional color have been cropping up in England. The United Kingdom's Atomic Energy Authority (U.K.A.E.A.) employs color at most of its installations. Let's look at some of the ways our English cousins exploit industrial color.

External color. The majority of the Authority's buildings are asbestos-clad with patent glazing for economy reasons. Gutters and drainpipes are vivid primary colors and white; so are doors, pipe bridges, and walkways—the reason: "to give a bright and cheerful appearance to buildings, even on dull days . . ." and to identify entrances and major plant items by color reference.

Internal treatment of buildings. Steel framework is a light ash gray, walls pastel shades, and ceilings white. "This is to achieve the effect of spaciousness, light and cleanliness" and to form a suitable background for the vividly colored plant.

Color treatment of machinery. According to the U.K.A.E.A., ". . . machinery, being the essential part of the project, is painted in gay colors. The large items of plant are painted in paler shades, and the small items in vivid full colors." Overhead cranes wear their moving parts in bright red as a danger warning. Electric switches and guard rails are similarly painted. The atomic-powered turbines are in different bright colors, partly for easy identification and partly to avoid predominance of any particular color. There is a method to this. "Internal color schemes are arranged so that . . . as a whole a correct composition in color exists. An unlimited number of abstract compositions in color can be achieved in different sections of the plant. Clear and bright colors . . . give cheerful surroundings . . . for workers . . . one of the essential conditions for keeping workers happy and encouraging cleanliness."

The U.K.A.E.A.'s color plans avoid changes in color on a particular piece of plant or structure. This means that a turbine is only one color; so is an escape stair. On the other hand, when a fan and its motor are separate and connected only by a belt, separate colors are used. The common base plate then is painted a third color.

Pipes are painted to blend into the general color scheme, but they are banded to indicate their function.

In carrying out its program, the U.K.A.E.A. developed a range of twelve colors: pale yellow, pale blue, pink, pale green, bright yellow, bright blue, bright red, bright green, dark blue, maroon, black, and white. It gave manufacturers swatches of these colors to match in painting the plant. When its plants are repainted the color scheme will be changed to break up monotony and add new interest.

What does the U.K.A.E.A. think about its color planning?

"It is worthwhile noting that it costs no more to apply colored paint . . . in fact the output of painters increases on pleasant color schemes . . . the output of operatives is improved by working in a happy atmosphere of color."

Sounds famliiar.

SOME EASY RULES TO FOLLOW

Let us look at some of the ways functional color can work most profitably for you and *your* workers.

Functional color for work areas. The fundamental aim in selecting colors for such areas is to provide a welcome lift to your employees' morale and to their productiveness. The proper selection of colors can bring sunshine into normally dark areas, create a cool atmosphere, and minimize eyestrain by avoiding too harsh contrasts in brightness between adjacent surfaces.

Functional color for rest areas. In such spaces, proper color styling can create a cheerful, restful atmosphere. Here, as in all places in your plant, proper lighting is also essential.

Functional color for safety. Traditionally, red has stood for

99

fire, green for safety, red, orange, or yellow for danger. These and other colors can be worked into a co-ordinated safety code which protects the worker and prepares for an emergency—purple warns of atomic-radiation perils, for example. All aisles, traffic lanes, and stairs can be clearly marked by painting them in colors contrasting to the body of the floor, or by using strong, contrasting colors as boundary lines.

Accent colors on machinery separate critical from noncritical parts, resulting in a reduction in accident rates; operating parts are given a quickly perceptible color which is in strong but not dazzling contrast to the stationary or noncritical parts. This so-called *focal color* focuses the attention of the worker exactly where it belongs and helps to reduce the unnecessary and fatiguing eye travel which occurs when the whole machine is painted in a single color.

Functional machine color is most effective when the focal colors provide a satisfactory contrast with both stationary parts and the material flowing through the machine. When this double contrast is achieved, eye travel is discouraged and tension is reduced. The result of this improved visibility soon makes itself felt in the daily output of the worker—and in his attitude toward his work.

Mobile equipment should be painted in high-visibility danger-signal colors to warn workers of its approach. Similar colors should be used on any cranes or overhead conveyors that dip down to head height or lower at certain stations.

Movable bins used to collect or distribute materials should also be treated with colors that shout for attention. The insides of the bins should be given a color that will contrast with their contents, thus making it easy to see just how much material a bin contains.

The American Car and Foundry Company, when it received Pennsylvania's Special Award for Safety, gave painting major credit for earning the award.

FUNCTIONAL COLOR
FOR PIPE IDENTIFICATION

The use of distinguishing colors for pipe identification plays an important role in maintaining plant operations at high efficiency and eliminating waste resulting from mishandling of materials.

Piping colors have been established by the American Standards Association. They include:

Red—FIRE PROTECTION (including sprinkler system)

Yellow or *Orange*—DANGEROUS MATERIALS (inflammable or poisonous)

Green, White, Black, Gray, or *Aluminum*—SAFE MATERIALS

Light Blue—PROTECTIVE MATERIALS (antidotes to poisonous fumes, for example)

Purple—VALUABLE MATERIALS

REFLECTIVE FLOORS

Under certain circumstances, the under portions of products being fabricated require more than the usual illumination. An example is an airplane wing; there good working visibility is essential below as well as above. Similar conditions generally prevail in the fabrication of all large objects which cannot be readily turned over for better observation. The problem is solved by increasing the reflectivity of the floor, thereby diffusing proper light to the underside of the product being worked on.

STANDARDIZATION OF COLORS

Although many industries realize the value of functional color, there is a disturbing lack of uniformity in their safety-painting standards, a lack which deserves special attention. One plant may have a safety color scheme entirely different from its neighbor's. This diversity can wreck an employee's spontaneity of action during an emergency, especially if the worker has been moving from one plant to another.

101

There is need for a standardized color code for industrial plants. It should have these aims:

1. Establishing particular colors for specific devices or conditions.
2. Indicating the location of hazards or protective devices and enabling the worker to guide his actions accordingly.
3. Assisting in the maintenance of proper working conditions, encouraging good housekeeping, and keeping employee morale high.

Recognizing this need, paint manufacturers are now featuring industrial safety colors. Here is their color code:

YELLOW—indicates *strike-against, stumbling, falling, or tripping hazards.*

ORANGE—marks *parts of machines or equipment that might cut or crush a worker.*

RED—identifies *fire equipment.*

GREEN—identifies *first-aid equipment, dispensaries, and other safety areas or devices.*

BLUE—warns against use of *equipment under repair or other machinery that should not be operated.*

WHITE or YELLOW—marks *aisles* and directs *the flow of traffic.*

Many factories are using these colors to spotlight various areas and equipment, but the effectiveness of this marking depends on universal adoption of these standards. Instant recognition is as important as high visibility. Industry and public authorities would do well to reach an agreement on standardizing color signals, perhaps through the establishment of a color clearing house to centralize and evaluate industrial color information.

INDUSTRIAL COLOR
MAKES GOOD NEIGHBORS

Color can be important outside the factory, too. More and

more communities are showing intense concern about their appearance. Art and architectural commissions, planning boards, and other public agencies are having an increasing amount to say about the maintenance and construction of buildings—including industrial buildings.

Community appearance is even falling under the legislative eye. Not long ago, A. S. Bard, writing in the *American Journal of Economics and Sociology,* cited interesting court decisions on the subject of aesthetics and the police power of the state. He quotes a U.S. Supreme Court opinion:

Miserable and disreputable housing conditions may do more than spread disease and crime and immorality. They may also suffocate the spirit by reducing the people who live there to the status of cattle. . . . They may also be an ugly sore, a blight on the community which robs it of its charm. . . . The concept of public welfare is broad and inclusive . . . it is within the power of the legislature to determine that the community should be beautiful as well as healthy, spacious as well as clean, well-balanced as well as carefully patrolled.

Mr. Bard, commenting on this decision, states, "Not until the courts recognize beauty as a ground for the exercise of police power by the state or community on the same basis that they fully recognize health, safety, morality, and good order as grounds for such exercise, and as an equal partner with those factors in the term 'community welfare,' will planning and the law of planning come full circle."

With the community's increased awareness of what it looks like, factories and other industrial establishments can ill afford to maintain the dispiriting drabness that too often leaves its bleak mark on American industry. As was mentioned in connection with the Esso and Phillips refineries, a planned exterior color scheme for your plant can improve maintenance and raise employee morale. That color plan can also go far to help your buildings contribute to the improving appearance of the American community.

HOW ABOUT INDUSTRIAL LIGHTING?

In the last chapter we saw that lighting and color had to work hand in hand in the store. So it is with the factory. Correct lighting is a key coworker with functional color—good lighting can bolster and bad lighting can botch color's contribution to increasing efficiency and production.

Studies by the Better Vision Institute point up the toll on eyes from improper color and lighting. One of every three workers in this country needs glasses; 40 per cent of all workers are visually unqualified for their jobs. Among office and textile workers, 50 per cent have faulty vision; among garment workers, 75 per cent. At the age of fifteen, 23 per cent of the people in the United States have defective eyesight; by age fifty, the percentage has climbed to 71; above age sixty, to more than 95 per cent. These increases are not due to advancing age alone. The statistics point to the need for much more efficient use of color and lighting in work areas.

Because it can be rigidly standardized at all times of day, artificial illumination often promotes greater efficiency and safety than regular daylight. Visibility depends on good illumination, but good illumination does not necessarily mean more light. Lighting engineers and color specialists work to achieve glareless lighting and clear but restful contrasts.

PROPER LIGHT
REFLECTION IS IMPORTANT

In any work area there are three general sources of reflected light which affect the eyes: (1) the ceiling and walls; (2) the eye-level area comprising the dado, work benches, machines, and the like; (3) the floor.

Any violent contrast in brightness between these areas can be trying to a worker's eyes. Most people do not realize that much of the fatigue and many of the headaches which arise during the working day result from excessive glare and extremely high brightness contrasts.

When workers, after a period of intent work at dark machines, look up at a dazzling surrounding surface with 70 to 80 per cent reflection, their eyes automatically attempt to accommodate themselves to the task of seeing under this new condition. The pupils of their eyes contract quickly—then start dilating immediately when the eyes are withdrawn from the surrounding view and put back to work. This cycle, repeated hundreds of times a day, often causes serious eyestrain and is extremely fatiguing.

The answer to this problem is found in painting the two reflecting areas—the area where the worker's eye rests and the area that he sees when he is concentrating—to represent near-identical reflectance values. While high-reflecting whites and creams are desirable from the standpoint of decreasing lighting costs, such colors should be used only on ceilings high enough to be above the worker's line of vision. Otherwise they contrast too violently with machine and product colors.

Differences in brightness up to 20 per cent are usually not disturbing. When we decrease the light reflectance of walls in order to conform to this limit, we can often lighten the color of the floor at the same time so that the total light reflectance in the work area is not lowered. Paints having up to 40 per cent light reflectance are now available for floors.

With the exception of yellow, colors will not reflect light efficiently if too far removed in value from white. White itself soils easily, often lacks eye appeal, and can create excessive contrast. Soft, restful shades like light gray, pale green, and light blue make the best line-of-vision colors. Light gray is especially practical because it is an effective dirt concealer as well.

The approximate light reflectance of various paint colors, in descending order, is shown in the accompanying table; of course, the reflectance varies with different pigments and different manufacturers.

105

COLOR	LIGHT REFLECTANCE PER CENT
White	83
Cream	78
Yellow	75
Golden yellow	72
Light pink	70
Tan	60
Gray	55
Light blue	55
Light green	51
Orange	50
Rust	40
Turquoise	40
Lavender	40
Royal blue	35
Maroon	30
Dark green	20
Red	15
Brown	15
Olive	10
Purple	10

THREE RULES

The amount of light a worker requires depends on the color of his work surface and his surroundings, on the kind of work he is doing with his eyes, and on his age. For anyone doing eye work, we can prevent strain, fatigue, and nervous tension by applying these simple rules:

(1) avoid gloom—use enough light.
(2) avoid glare—use glareless light.
(3) avoid dark shadows.
(4) avoid excessive contrast.

THE AWAKENING IN INDUSTRY

How important proper lighting can be in modern industrial

planning is emphasized in a *Wall Street Journal* article of December 14, 1955. Here is the *Journal's* headline:

"FACTORIES TRIM COSTS,
INCREASE PRODUCTION
WITH BETTER LIGHTING
Milwaukee Firm Notes Drop in Absentees:
Cincinnati Plant Has Fewer Accidents."

The article starts off by citing a Fisher Body plant in Grand Rapids, Michigan, where eight hundred women turning out Chevrolet interior fabrics complained that they were seeing spots, circles, and dots in front of their eyes. "A preliminary check of lighting conditions," said the newspaper, "disclosed that at sewing machines where the women work the intensity of light, measured by metering equipment, is twelve to twenty time brighter than in surrounding parts of their work area. This contrast is apparently what's causing the women to see things that aren't there." The report added: "The Fisher Body Division of General Motors Coroporation is investigating the matter further, and says more than likely an improvement of the lighting setup will result. Industry's spending for improved factory lighting is scooting upwards, and if the experience of other businessmen is any guide, G. M. officials at Grand Rapids will find the money spent will be more than repaid in higher output per worker, lower production costs and a generally happier, healthier and probably safer work force."

The story goes on to relate how much industry is spending for lighting installations in the new plants and in lighting improvements in older plants; it cites many examples of what firms have already done. The Allis-Chalmers Manufacturing Company, for example, "found that a combination of increased lighting and interior repainting cut accident frequency about 50 percent in a Milwaukee plant. To achieve this result, foot-candle output of its high-ceiling lighting equipment was quadrupled, and the plant interior was repainted—the ceiling a light blue, sidewalls light green, and travelng cranes yellow."

107

COLOR'S CONTRIBUTION WILL GROW

The color and lighting innovations we've discussed in this chapter are not separable. When we shoot for one, we usually get the others. Good visibility, efficient lighting, colors which do not strain the eyes, spatial color functionally used—all these add up to harmony, beauty, and employee morale. Higher morale means better work. One thing is certain. Dollars spent in improving color and lighting always means greater safety and efficiency and they pay off in less waste and larger output.

Today, all over the nation, color engineering—functional color and co-ordinated lighting—is helping to win the fight against needless accidents and inefficiency. The color engineer's contribution grows continually as its value becomes more widely recognized and its benefits more widely understood by plant management and worker alike.

A Shell Oil Company executive sums up the industrial advantages of correct color use very well. "A man driving a new auto takes care of his car. The same is true of a drilling rig. Our object at Shell in adopting a color code was to improve housekeeping, believing it would also improve our safety record. We've won on both counts."

COLOR IN TRANSPORTATION:
SAFETY AND SALES

Some years ago a Florida attorney, thirty-four years old and earning $45,000 a year, attempted to inhabit a grade crossing at the same time as a Florida East Coast Railway Diesel locomotive. He failed. His executor sued the railroad.

One of the charges of negligence set out in the suit alleged that the lawyer could not have seen the locomotive, although the accident happened on a straight stretch of track at mid-afternoon on a clear day. Since this count involved some technical considerations that are the stock-in-trade of the color engineer, I was called as a witness.

I found that the Florida East Coast locomotive was wearing a chrome-yellow and scarlet paint job, and at the time of the accident was moving against a background of green foliage. Nothing could have made the train more visible at that place and that time; if the lawyer had been looking for the train he would have seen it and so I stated.

The jury found for the railroad. The Florida East Coast Railway had received a peculiarly effective return on its investment in color in transporation.

The color engineer finds a broad field of work in the transportation business. Correct color can be a big factor in safety. Correct color can produce happier passengers and more of them. Let's look at some of the color uses which are producing dividends for the transportation industry today.

COLOR AND SAFETY

Whether you're flying a thousand-mile-an-hour jet or walking on two-mile-an-hour feet, the pace of modern transportation means you often have scant seconds to see the plane or train or ship or car coming at you and to get out of the way before it eliminates your chances to avoid similar hazards in the future. If we can extend the range of your vision, we can give you more time to take evasive action. Fortunately, color can do just that.

Consider the Train

If that Florida lawyer's unfortunate encounter with a locomotive had taken place on the trackage of the New York Central or the Pennsylvania, either railroad might very well have found itself out something over a hundred thousand dollars. The Central's locomotives are gray; the Pennsy's black. Both color schemes effectively camouflage the locomotive wearing them, camouflage which differs from its military uses in that is spells not safety but death.

The late-lamented steam locomotive announced its imminence with a ferocious succession of respiratory noises and a column of smoke. Its successor, the Diesel, purrs instead of pants and emits gas fumes instead of smoke. That means that the old stop-look-and-listen procedure doesn't work so well any more; it won't work at all unless you give prospective victims something to look for. That's where the color engineer comes in.

What colors he develops for your locomotive will depend on the trackage that locomotive's going to run on. One Pacific Coast railroad had its locomotives painted green and yellow. They blended nicely into California's foilage. Next the railroad

110

tried black and silver. It was fine in California but useless in the Nevada desert. The color engineer prescribed black and orange, the single color combination which could work well along the entire length of that railroad's right-of-way.

New York's Long Island Railroad, which seems to have enough troubles without color problems, scrapped its old Tuscan red train color and substituted a field gray. The Long Island's employees liked it fine but motorists didn't; it merged with the Island's hedgerows, especially in mist or at dusk. I worked on that one. I kept the gray and prescribed a bright orange for the locomotive's ends. It contrasted with the gray and stood out against the hedges. Motorists stopped complaining.

For the Central Railroad of New Jersey, a line which winds through the lush greens of Monmouth County and the bleak grays of Jersey City, I developed a conspicuous orange-and-blue locomotive color plan. Used together, these two colors enhance each other, picking up extra visual impact and producing exceptional long-range visibility.

Consider the Airplane

Two major mid-air collisions between passenger aircraft—the Grand Canyon crash in 1956 which killed 128 people and the Michigan City crash in 1953 which fortunately killed nobody—took place in relatively clear weather under visual flying conditions and between aircraft flying almost parallel courses. If they had seen each other, the participants could have avoided the crashes. Spotting the other plane before you hit it is only one aspect of the nagging problem of preventing mid-air collisions; the other factors range from the gaps in the air-traffic control system to a discouraging phenomenon called altitude myopia. Whatever contribution these other factors may have made to the Grand Canyon and the Michigan City and the other 150-odd mid-air collisions over the last ten years, the fact remains that most of them occurred in clear weather and that in most of them pilots simply didn't see each other. Color can't make the

111

pilot look out of the cockpit, but it can help him see another plane when he starts looking.

Color has its limitations in making aircraft more conspicuous. When a plane is more than ten miles away, for example, it's impossible to distinguish its color at all. And the varying backgrounds against which a plane must be seen—ground, snow, water, and a multitude of cloud types—mean that it's hard to develop a high-conspicuity color plan which will work even if you can see the plane. Certain colors do help in certain circumstances, however.

The Navy, for example, is now painting its training planes, and air-sea rescue aircraft in a split color plan of international orange and glossy white; the new colors are specially valuable to tower operators when the plane is in the landing pattern.

The Air Force has found that a split color plan of red and aluminum makes its planes more visible under Arctic conditions.

The Civil Aeronautics Authority is experimenting with an Ercoupe dressed in Day-Glo fluorescent orange paint (manufactured by Switzer Brothers).

None of these are all-purpose high-visibility schemes. There is probably no single color plan which can work under all conditions. The problem, as the Air Force's Dr. Walter F. Grether points out, is not relative color but relative brightness—a black plane would show up best against a white cloud, but in fog or smog it would be the least visible. Be this as it may, it is discouraging to find that the airlines, of all businesses, fail to take advantage of color's limited benefit. The silver-and-white commercial airliner of today wears a color scheme which is singularly ill-suited to most flying conditions. The Navy's orange-and-white would clearly improve short-range conspicuity; the color engineer can put his finger on other color plans which can do this important job equally well. Color is no collision cure-all but it can help. If the world's transport airlines fail to take advantage of this help they may, wittingly or unwittingly, be helping to encourage the next mid-air crash.

Color can enchance aircraft safety inside the cockpit, too. One of the biggest problems in flying results from the pilot's constant shifting of his vision from inside the cockpit to outside and back again. The more contrast he faces in making this visual shift, the more fatiguing it can be. This means that in daylight we want the inside of the cockpit bright; at night we want it dark. One way we can help solve this problem is by using a gray and maroon color plan in the cockpit; the colors have reasonable reflectivity during the day, and darken under red light at night.

The red light poses another problem. Most aircraft use red cockpit light to enable the eye to adjust to night seeing—red light does the least to blind that part of the eye which does most of the visual work at night. On the other hand the Swedish Navy has found that brown light works even better than red at this job. One of the problems my firm is currently studying is the effect of different light colors on the mechanism of the eye—a study crucially important to flying safety as well as to safety of other kinds.

Consider the Automobile

Cars are color-styled to consider anything but safety. Some of the current car color plans blend so nicely with normal road backgrounds that they would delight the eye of the military camoufleur. This is not the fault, primarily, of the automobile companies. They are spraying on the paint jobs which consumers have voted for with that most potent of all ballots—the dollar. But consumers are learning that other factors than appearance are involved. You may take note of this the next time you drive behind a car with high-reflectivity tape stripped on its back bumper. The consumer is beginning to realize the safety value of color, and one of these days he may decide that what's good for his back bumper will be even better for his whole car. It may be a long way off, but I'm betting that some

113

time in the future a car manufacturer is going to pick off a good slice of the automobile business with a car color-styled not just for looks but for both appearance and safety.

This is equally true of buses. Too many modern buses, seeking the economy of colors which don't show dirt, wear drab industrial colors to match their drab industrial backgrounds. A bus is a big target and an effective projectile. The wise use of color can help it avoid performing either of these two discouraging functions.

Consider the Ship

Take a ferry ride around your favorite harbor some time. You'll find most of its shipping dressed in colors so conservative that they look as if they've just steamed out of a Victorian yacht club. Black hull and white superstructure—the modern ship draws its colors from the riotous garb of the penguin. Only funnels and flags supply color to the run-of-the-harbor ship, and even these are often gloomy and colorless and, worst of all, invisible. There's no good reason for this drabness except for the durable conservatism which seems to attach so often to things nautical. A colorful ship is a more visible ship. The same considerations which apply to airplanes and trains and cars apply equally well at sea. A few seconds can make the difference between close shave and catastrophe. If the *Andrea Doria* had been wearing a high-visibility paint job there is just the possibility that she might be afloat today. The fact that such a possibility exists would have made a high-visibility color plan eminently worth while.

I've applied just such a color plan to a pair of maritime maids-of-all-work which find themselves concerned with collisions as an everyday part of their business: tugboats and ferries. When I went to work on the Central Railroad of New Jersey's tugs and ferries they were a low-visibility olive drab. They became a high-visibility green and white; they look better, people like them better, and they're a lot less apt to get run down by a hurrying tugboat. Regrettably, most of today's shipping execu-

114

Pittsburgh Plate Glass Company, Jones and Laughlin Steel Corporation

The utilization of the energy in color not only adds to the pleasing appearance of this machine but is an integral part of its functioning. The dark green over-all color is in restful contrast to the important control sections so that these can be watched without eyestrain. Moving parts are painted an attention-arresting orange. Vital levers are bright red, making them easy to see and to grasp.

The precisely right colors for packaging and for products
can be superlatively persuasive.

When it was found necessary to add a third pump to the brilliant green and red pumps that characterize Cities Service stations, clear primary yellow solved the problem. All three pumps are banded in white in the same design. Result: attention-compelling color in a framework of identifying unity.

Arkansas Fuel Oil Corporation
(Annual Report)

Typical Ketcham color plan for a private room in a hospital. A cheerful creamy pink is the dominant color. No sharply contrasting colors are used so that the over-all effect is restful and soothing. There is no monotony because the dark and light surfaces of the furniture are picked up in both the color and the design in the draperies.

Hill-Rom Company, Inc.

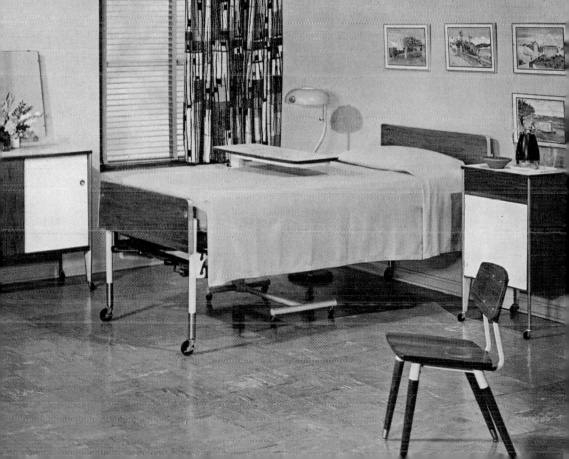

General Electric Company

The treatment of this kitchen tends to become a little monotonous because both the pink and the finish of the wood are warm colors. A contrasting, cooler accent, such as Delft blue, would do much to make this room a more satisfying working area. In the laundry there is just enough of the fairly intense turquoise equipment to make an interesting color corner in the warm reddish setting of the wood paneling. The sparing touches of pink blend with the wood finish.

American Telephone and Telegraph Company

As functional as it is gay, this kitchen wall telephone helps to brighten the work of the homemaker. The soft, slightly golden shade of yellow has been created by the author to blend successfully with a wide variety of hues. Black telephones were supplanted within three years by 10,000,000 telephones in eight different Ketcham colors.

Rohm and Haas Company—Star Market Company

An outstanding example of illuminated Plexiglas makes the star emblem and lettering memorable at night. It is less effective in the daytime when the supporting structure of the star is visible and the boxes of the separate letters have a rather distracting effect.

tives, with a wary eye on maintenance costs, persist in painting their ships as if they are going to slug it out with a pack of U-boats as soon as they clear the channel.

Consider the Highway

Highway markings vary from state to state and sometimes from community to community. The double white line in one town becomes a single yellow line just across the border. There are correct colors for highways just as well as for almost everything else. For today's highway, the key color is yellow.

A strong-chroma yellow has three advantages as a highway marking paint.

1. It provides the greatest contrast and therefore the greatest conspicuity against a dark surface.
2. It shows up in contrast with snow.
3. Drivers associate it with both attention and danger.

The right yellow is the same one specified for highway signs— a chrome yellow, normally produced as a lead chromate pigment.

Yellow should be used where we want to say "Watch out!" and say it loud. This means yellow should be used for:

> Center lines
> No-passing zones
> Stop lines
> Railroad crossings
> Pedestrian crossings

White is permissible on:

> Lane lines
> Pavement edges
> Streetcar-clearance lines
> Turn markings
> Parking-space limits
> Route directions

115

Markings on vertical surfaces of objects in the roadway or near it should consist of alternate black and white stripes; the new high-reflective paints are also good for these. It is useful to slap white on guard rails, trees, and rocks near the road. An especially useful place for color is the right edge of the road— too many of today's highways shade off into a twilight zone of gas-station approaches, driveways, and plain soft shoulders. The night driver, faced with a procession of powerful high-beam headlights zeroed in on his windshield, does lots of his driving with his eyes on the shoulder of the road. If there's a stripe— yellow or white—along that shoulder, it will help him stay on course. This aid can also be all-important at other times of low visibility— in fog, rain, or twilight.

Traffic lights pose some color problems, too. There are very few truly color-blind people; most of the people we call color-blind trip over only certain reds and greens. This means that the good traffic light is not red and green in the conventional sense at all. The green must be a blue-green and the red a yellow-red; the red-green blind will still see blue and yellow.

The position of these colors is also important in helping the color-blind. The *Manual on Uniform Traffic Control Devices,* published by the American Association of State Highway Officials, suggests the following standard arrangement for the colored lenses in a traffic light. From top to bottom, or left to right, you should see: (1) red, (2) yellow, (3) green.

How about highway signs? As we've noted, the standard color for the operational signs—the signs that tell you about cross streets, schools, and deer crossings—is a high-visibility yellow. Fine. They tell you where to stop. But what about those signs which tell you where to go? Route markers have a discouraging propensity for being small, colorless, and unreadable. Some states, however—Massachusetts is one—color-code their highways; if a motorist knows that Route 128, say, is marked with green-and-white signs he's going to have less trouble staying on Route 128. It is a good and sensible practice, and I'd like to see it extended.

116

One good way it can be extended is by putting the color not only on the sign but also on the road. This is now commercially feasible; adding color to concrete is not prohibitively expensive and there are pigments available which won't fade objectionably. England's Ministry of Transport has already experimented with coloring highways in the Channel Isles. John R. W. Smail, a long-time resident of those Isles, has pointed out that "it is an idea which could well be extended to the Colonies." Colored roads would make route-following a lead-pipe cinch except in deep snow; the correct color, furthermore, could cut down sun and headlight glare from the road surface. Some day soon you may follow Route One from Maine to Florida by color—you'll take the high road and I'll take the yellow road and I'll be in Florida afore ye.

COLOR FOR HABITABILITY

"Habitability" is a Navy word, nowadays. It deals with the problem of making places more comfortable to live in and work in. We all know how color can make the home or office a better place to inhabit—we're going to discuss those aspects of habitability later in the book. But one of color's more remarkable habitability jobs has been in the field of transportation, and we're going to discuss some of those applications now.

Follow the Fleet

Before World War II color planning for the Navy was no mammoth job. Ships were gray outside and gray inside, a supply officer's delight but a source of unmitigated gloom to everybody else.

The war's injection of less stoic and less gloom-prone reservists into this gray world caused some changes. As ships came in for refit their officers hired professional help and brightened up compartments—often paying for the job out of their pockets and violating a formidable wad of regulations in the process. The officers and crewmen liked the new cheerfulness and said

117

so. When the war ended and the Navy had time to work on the problem, it initiated a formal study of the ways color could make life aboard ship more attractive.

The first experimental color plans were worked up by the Medical Research Laboratory for some submarines based at New London. The new frigate *Mitscher* got a color plan in 1948; the experimental destroyer *Meredith* in 1952. The plans worked and people liked them. Today's Navy takes considerable color to sea with it.

The new color schemes are written into the specifications for all new construction—prospective commanding officers can modify these color schemes if the changes won't run into extra cost or time. On existing ships the C.O.'s or their representatives choose the new colors or materials when the ship comes in for refit.

The Navy gives its skippers a palette of colors to choose from: beach sand, clipper blue, rosewood, sun glow, white, pastel green, green gray, yellow gray, and pastel blue. Upholstery material—selected to be sturdy, fire-resistant, and color-compatible—comes in cordovan, yew green, crimson, blue, and sandalwood. Deck tile, lightweight and equally fire-resistant, is available in marbleized patterns: black and white; red and white; green and white; gray, black and white; black, white, and terra cotta; charcoal, red, and white. The new colors are now at work on ships ranging from the nuclear-powered *Nautilus* to the giants *Forrestal* and *Saratoga*. Nicolaus Bruns, Jr., head of the Bureau of Ships Legislative and Special Matters Section, sums up the program this way: "Considerable evidence has indicated that the forces afloat are well pleased with the new look."

Habitability Color and How It Works

The key to the Navy's success in using color to make its ships better living places lies in those psychological color mechanics we talked about in our chapters on stores and factories. Color can make small spaces look bigger, break up the monotony of exteriors, cool warm spaces and warm cool ones, stimulate people where we want them stimulated and lull them where we want them lulled. The color engineer has a big bag of tricks at his disposal, and habitability color planning extends to a far wider field in transportation than the warship.

Buses

A distraught New York City businessman recently defined the bus as "an ambulatory sewer pipe with an exit door at one end and all the passengers standing at the other." Bus passengers are a surly lot—some years ago a *New Yorker* correspondent found an irate old lady assaulting a bus with her umbrella handle in retribution for several grievances the bus had inflicted on her. Part of the trouble is that the run-of-the-street bus is such a singularly unattractive conveyance to inhabit.

The average bus consists of a long cigar-like enclosure, monotonous and gloomy. It looks cramped and even more crowded than it is, and if it incorporates any of several color schemes I've seen, it makes its passengers appear even more bilious yellow than they may feel. This atmosphere might be appropriate for an eighteenth-century slave ship, but it's hardly conducive to convincing passengers that "it's more comfortable by bus."

Fortunately color can do a great deal to dispel this dismal atmosphere. For one bus line, for example, we developed a color plan incorporating a soft, receding blue on the ceiling. It worked so well that some of its passengers thought they were getting into a double decker when they climbed aboard.

For New York's Carey Transportation, Inc., we worked to rid their airport limousines of an extraordinary bleak interior— made all the worse because passengers saw it right before or right after riding in the thoroughly non-bleak atmosphere of latter-day aircraft. Carey hired us when a newspaper columnist remarked that passengers alighting in New York went from an airplane to a hearse. Color planning converted the Carey limousines into more appropriate conveyances.

119

For New York's Fifth Avenue Coach Company we have designed color plans to make the buses look bigger and less crowded, and—joy to the bus driver—to help keep passengers moving to the rear. This latter job was done by using contrasting colors in the rear part of the bus to convey a feeling of openness and space. The lighting was tailored to compliment the complexion of women riders. The yellow woman bus rider is a prospective subway rider; if we can light her attractively (and we can, through color planning and color-corrected lighting) we can help keep her riding the bus.

Some bus companies, realizing that the inhospitable interior is a superb way of sending passengers scurrying home by some other means of conveyance, have polled their passengers on what colors they would like to ride amidst. This carrying of the case to the people is sound in principle but dangerous in practice; the public's choice is too often dictated by some unexpected considerations. In Kansas City, for example, the bus operators polled their people in the summer—the passengers voted for a cool apple green. In Washington, D.C., where the bus riders voted in the winter, they selected a warm tan. Climate is only one of the extraneous factors which can creep into color planning when you leave it entirely up to the consumer. It takes a color engineer to keep these factors out, and to give the bus rider colors which he *and* she will like all year round.

Airplanes

Color, both inside and out, can increase the habitability of aircraft.

On the outside, color can do much to control the plane's interior temperature. White is an excellent heat reflector; in a test exposure a piece of white-painted aluminum kept twenty-eight degrees cooler than a similar piece left unpainted. The Air Force and Navy use this phenomenon to protect their planes from the heat radiation of an atomic blast; some airlines now take advantage of it to keep their passengers cooler. A DC–6 with a glossy-white upper exterior can run as much as ten degrees cooler than the same plane, same place, unpainted. Fortunately, glossy white combines nicely with orange to supply one of the high-visibility color plans we talked about in our section on safety.

On the inside, color and illumination planning can make the plane look larger, sturdier, and safer. It can break up the discomforting sameness of the commercial aircraft's structure and give passengers a feeling of well-being.

As a case history let's take a look at that outgrowth of the wartime B–29, the big Boeing Stratocruiser which today is still flying some of the aviation industry's longest hauls. I had done color and design planning for Pan American World Airways since PAA was flying Ford trimotors; when PAA ordered $37,000,000 worth of Stratocruisers, I went to work on their interiors.

The Stratocruiser is aviation's duplex apartment, with a sixty-six-foot upper deck which makes it look like an airborne tunnel. To make it look less tunnel-like, I foreshortened the long row of seats by using one color up to the middle and another color from there to the rear of the plane. The forward seats are blue-green, the rear seats beige. The curtains reverse this arrangement. To get greater height, the rest of the cabin interior colors grow progressively lighter in value from the deep blue of the carpet to the light-reflecting bisque overhead. Similar treatments expand the lower-deck lounge.

The Stratocruiser's successors present some of the same problems, some different. They are even bigger, and their structures are dictated by the aerodynamics of jet speeds. Color must play a big part in making them habitable.

Habitability Color Pays

Planes and buses are just two of the many forms of modern transportation which can put habitability color to work to their profit. Trains, ships, passenger cars: all of them supply fertile fields for the feeling of well-being and visual value color can create.

COLOR:
KEY TO TRANSPORTATION PERSONALITY

We've already seen color at work promoting safety and increasing habitability. Color can do a third job in transporation, too. That's the important job of building a personality for your transporation facilities, a personality that sells.

There are myriad ways in which color can do this, but let's touch on a sampling of them.

Ferries

We've already seen how color can make the ferryboat more visible. The same colors can make the ferry more attractive and more enjoyable, and can give passengers a lift. Our Jersey Central ferries have the squat, bulldog design which makes them and most of their sisters of other lines look like the *Monitor* on its way to visit the *Merrimac*. We minimized this dumpy appearance with a color plan which uses progressively lighter colors from the waterline to the upper deck. It looks better and customers like it better. We know. They've said so.

Yachts

Yachts share with their larger siblings the lackluster conservatism which makes for bleak dullness afloat. When we went to work for the Century Boat Company we felt that this conservatism was rooted in tradition, not in demand—that the same color and design preferences which had revolutionized the automobile business applied equally well to yachts. We restyled Century's line accordingly, incorporating the two-tone paint jobs, hard tops, and wrap-around-windshields that you find on today's cars. The results were extraordinary. Century's Coronada cruiser, for example, promptly sold out, piling up a backlog of three years' orders in the process.

Trucks

Most trucks still ride around in the colors of economy, in the

122

olive drabs, browns, and grays which hide dirt. You don't put your color advertising or packaging in dirt-hiding colors, however, and there's no reason why you should do so with your truck. The truck is an ambulatory advertisement—with the correct color plan it can convey dignity (for prestige merchandise), cleanliness (for food), gaiety (for flowers). It can make the truck look bigger or smaller. It can carry out the colors of your trademark, store, merchandise, products, or what have you. An integrated color-merchandising campaign fails to cash in on all the possibilities if it ignores the truck. New York's Chock Full O'Nuts luncheonettes have service trucks designed to simulate a Chock Full O'Nuts store on wheels. There's integrated design and color for you, and a neat piece of advertising it is. You don't have to erect a house on your truckbed to take advantage of an integrated merchandising program, but that's the direction to go, nevertheless.

COLOR FOR AUTO SALES

Back in the 1920's, Edgar A. Guest wrote a poem: "Those New Auto Colors." * Here it is, reprinted with the author's permission.

> When I was but a little lad,
> Few were the colors that we had;
> Then red was red, and blue was blue,
> And that was all we ever knew:
> But since they've made the motor car
> Behold how many shades there are!
>
> Today I drove about the town
> In one dyed Piccadilly Brown.
> "There's one," I heard the driver say,
> "That's painted Arizona Gray.
> While that one at the other stand
> Is catalogued as Desert Sand."

* Copyright, 1925, by Edgar A. Guest.

123

They've named the colors for the streets,
For victories and great defeats,
For princes, presidents and kings,
Countries and states and endless things,
Fogs, mists, miasmas and the stars,
And painted them on motor cars.

There's London Fog, and Cactus Gray,
And Brewster Green, and few can say
Just which is which or what is what;
The name, I venture, matters not,
Give it a pretty phrase and nice,
The customer will pay the price.

Today I ought to be in bed,
My eyes with cold are Fireman's Red;
My food I cannot swallow down,
My mouth tastes Piccadilly Brown,
I'm feverish, faint, discouraged, too,
In fact, I feel Imperial Blue.

Mr. Guest had put his finger on one of the greatest bloomings of color in history—automobile color. Color may sell in other fields of transportation, but there's considerable evidence that it's a dominant factor in car sales. A few years before Mr. Guest's effort, Henry Ford had told his chief production man, Charles E. Sorensen, that Ford buyers could have "any color they want so long as it's black." Then Chevrolet began offering other colors, sales boomed, the competing automobile companies had to fall in line, and Mr. Guest had material for a poem. By the early 1930's Du Pont was offering more than thirteen thousand automobile finishes to manufacturers.

This didn't work, however. I found that out myself as the head of Du Pont's Color Advisory Service. Nobody needed thirteen thousand colors. The manufacturers didn't—they were inundated with paint. What I discovered was that the consumer didn't want them either. These were the depression years and what consumers wanted were economical, satisfying, and long-wearing colors, colors that wouldn't show dirt. The biggest-selling color during these years was black. As times got better color preferences changed to the brighter side—when a man can afford a new car and buys one he wants the neighbors to know it, and the best way he can do so is to get a bright and attractive car which doesn't look like his old one. So the desire for car color set in somewhere between the black days of Mr. Ford's twenties and the kaleidoscopic days of the early thirties.

As the fifties end, automobile companies are relying more than ever on styling and color for sales, and are spending huge amounts to make sure they have colors that will sell. Some are using survey techniques like the ones we describe in a later chapter; my firm completed a big survey for Dodge not too long ago. All of the companies employ extensive groups of people concerned with color. General Motors, for example, worries over its color problems in a 900-acre, $150-million technical center. Men like GM's Harley Earl and Chrysler's Virgil Exner and Ford's George Walker—all highly placed styling executives —are up to their knees in the color problem. They analyze sales popularity of past and present colors and correlate colors with the trends in home furnishings and high fashion, winding up first with color chips and then with large color panels which are worked over and worked over again until the colors are ready to go on actual cars. Then interior colors are developed to harmonize or contrast with the exterior colors.

The objectives of this procedure, as described by L. David Ash, another member of Ford's styling team, are:

1. To insure leadership colors with fashion correctness for the model year in which they are to be merchandised.
2. To obtain the greatest possible latitude in harmonizing and contrasting color combinations.
3. To make certain that colors will have wide acceptance with the consumer.

These are sensible objectives and they can be carried even further. The car companies are in a rough fight for the market, a fight that requires cutting costs on the inside and building sales on the outside, and in both, color can do more than it's doing. One of the persistent demands on the color engineer is for fewer colors, correct colors, for the colors people want. Color engineering can develop these colors and keep them so compatible with each other that they will permit more combinations than do present colors, and so that they will increase the diversity of color lines while they decrease the number of colors on hand. New materials can also help—lots of the new plastics and fabrics lend themselves to economy and sales appeal in automobile manufacture. The constant goal with color and material must be cutting costs on the one hand and increasing consumer demand on the other. It is in this direction, I believe, that the current car color competitor must go if he wants to end up a winner.

WHAT IT ADDS UP TO

We've seen a series of here-and-there examples of color doing things in transportation—making people happier, making them buy things, keeping them from running into one another. This boils down to an axiom that seems self-evident to the color engineer but not so obvious to a lot of other people. *Color is not just a form of decoration. It can do specific jobs.* Any "decorator" can make colors *look* well to his satisfaction and probably to yours. Making color *work* well is another problem, and one not susceptible to solution with a book of paint swatches and a nice eye for color co-ordination. The field of transportation, perhaps, embraces the most naked operational uses of color as a tool. It is a field which veritably shouts for the services of the color engineer.

HOW TO PLAN THE COLORS FOR YOUR PRODUCT

Look at your necktie collection when you have the chance. You'll find some ties wrinkled from constant wear and some as new-looking as they were when you bought them. Obviously, you prefer some of your ties to others. One reason is color. Every morning, when you pick your tie, you are a color consumer making a color choice. Every day 160 million color consumers make similar color choices. Color sells, and countless manufacturers are turning that fact to their own profit. Product color has become a paramount consideration in product design.

Compare one of today's newspapers or magazines with one that is ten or twenty years old—you'd hardly believe they were from the same century. Many of the old products have completely disappeared and new and startingly different ones have taken their places. Those that still exist are so different that you would hardly recognize them. The old-fashioned stark-white kitchen cabinet, for example, now appears in a wide and exciting range of color unheard of a generation ago. Today, 42 per cent of all steel kitchen cabinets are sold in color. The

127

demand for color in kitchens is still rising. General Electric reported that 20 per cent of their 1957 refrigerators were in color. One of the most dramatic and important changes in product planning over the years has been the sales-building addition of color.

In planning color specifications for both consumer and industrial products there are two basic requirements the progressive manufacturer should analyze and meet. First, the colors must serve a functional or utilitarian role—add to the product's usefulness or improve its operation. Second, the colors must have the widest possible appeal. Both of these requirements can be met and will be met if color selection is done through specialized techniques and skills.

Good color can affect a product in various ways. Here are six important ones:

1. Color improves ease of operation. For example, a machine with moving parts in correct contrasting colors is easier on the eyes and therefore easier to operate; it affords a greater degree of safety.

2. Color influences manufacturing costs.

3. Color signifies the quality, grade, size, and purpose of a product.

4. Color increases the scope of usefulness of a product.

5. Color makes products easy to locate and identify.

6. Color improves appearance and market acceptance.

Appearance improvement is the most obvious target of color application, for today, with workmanship, quality, and price so equal, good color appearance is the important factor in the success or failure of a product. It also helps to divert emphasis away from price.

Sometimes it is difficult to evaluate the color-appearance factor for a product without recourse to extensive and exacting market surveys, since many consumers, especially men, do not like to admit that they judge products by their looks.

Product design can never be hurt by good color planning.

Neat, appropriate, distinctive, and well-placed color arrangements result in a coherent impression. This provides a decided competitive advantage and generally at no extra cost. Furthermore, it is usually easy to improve a product's appearance through skillful color co-ordination without altering the product's performance, usefulness, or ease of operation and maintenance. Color can induce people to pay a premium price for a product, such as a colored telephone, and color, properly selected and properly introduced, can make an inexpensive product look more costly. People do not always consider colors simply from the viewpoint of their own individual and personal likes and dislikes. Instead, they tend to select colors they believe will impress their associates and acquaintances—the colors that it's "smart" to buy.

In improving product appearance through the application of color, the color engineer plans the approach to his work to answer these questions:

What is the function of the color plan?

What are the conditions of the product's use?

What colors do competitors employ?

Where will colors be applied on the product?

What psychological relationships are involved between consumer and product?

What background colors at point of sale require consideration?

Under what lighting will the colors be viewed?

COLOR FOR BETTER MARKETABILITY

The color styling and recoloring of products (used cars, for example) in most instances insures better marketability. All salesmen, dealers, and distributors have a substantial stake in the marketability of any product they handle; they must know the facts relating to the helpful and hindering aspects of a color line. Customers buy certain colors and reject others, and management must keep properly and promptly posted on con-

129

sumer color preferences. Product-color changes are sometimes costly and complicated, yet through the intelligent and correct anticipation of consumer color wants (and adroit color revision) management can frequently achieve better sales results—with less expense—than through far more costly design changes. The addition of colors to its rugged tire yarn gave American Enka Corporation a new quality market—automobile upholstery fabric. Color thus opened up a whole new area for selling.

A manufacturer's sales department needs product colors which will serve as a tool to build demand for his product. For example, machine tools and factory equipment require colors which promise more efficient operation—colors which improve morale, speed, and accuracy, and decrease absenteeism and accidents. In consumer products, the general facts that the color engineer has accumulated about consumer psychology, color, current taste, conditions of production, and the uses to which the individual product will be put are weighed and analyzed by him in planning the desirable color for the product.

Changing conditions often compel the adoption of radically different color schemes on manufactured products, another example of the close tie between color and marketability. When functional color schemes were adopted in progressive business offices, business machines in staid and conservative gray, black, and olive drab looked out of place and became out of date, and, of greater interest to the maker, out of demand. Colors in kitchen walls increased the clamor for color in home appliances. One stove manufacturer introduced compatible colors and realized 38 per cent of his sales in color during the next six months. Consumer demand for color has even outstripped the manufacturers; many home owners are sending out newly purchased appliances to automobile paint shops for refinishing in wanted colors, and a paint manufacturer has successfully introduced a special "porcelain finish" paint for appliances which the homemaker can apply in a single coat.

130

With this burgeoning use of color for home appliances and office equipment, more and more products are being revitalized by successful color engineering. Telephones are a case in point; they followed the typewriters, adding machines, and refrigerators in their break from traditional black and white. The once universal black phone will probably never be obsolete, but ever since cheerful phone colors were first introduced they have been acclaimed as a wonderful new method of adding accent color appeal to homes and offices. The eight colors that I created for telephones are designed to blend perfectly with both traditional and contemporary room and office decorating. Here is a list of the first eight colors offered and their special characteristics. The sequence is that of consumer preference in 1957.

IVORY: This versatile finish is unusually distinguished. It looks well anywhere, but especially in rooms and offices finished in light colors, or ones which have woodwork or trim in white or ivory with walls of any shade, dark or light.

BEIGE: This color takes on various hues in different settings. In boudoirs, beauty salons, or women's shops it can be made to appear almost rose-pink against a background of green or blue. But in an office or man's room it takes on the subdued tan tones of wood furniture.

GREEN: This is a true green, neither yellowish nor bluish, but an excellent shade of medium value and chroma. Its pleasant tone harmonizes well with other greens and contrasts agreeably with a number of complementary colors, in both homes and offices.

RED: This color has been especially created for use in offices as well as in homes. It is rich and full-bodied without being too bright. Thus it blends harmoniously with other shades of red, and yet is vivid enough to provide an arresting accent.

YELLOW: This soft, slightly golden shade blends successfully with a wide variety of hues, including other shades of yellow, from light lemon to deep buffs and ochers. It is popular in

131

kitchens, bedrooms, and wherever a light definite color is wanted.

BLUE: This medium-dark value is dark enough for a man's room or business office, but not too deep for a woman's room. Although it is muted enough to harmonize with most décors, it is a true blue that may be used with other shades of blue as well as with contrasting colors.

GRAY: This neutral color is particularly suitable for modern offices, with the new gray metal furniture and "eye-ease" desk tops. It is appropriate, however, anywhere that a practical instrument is needed because it does not show soil as readily as black or light colors.

BROWN: This finish has been designed to harmonize with all dark or natural woods, and can therefore be used effectively with any type of wooden furniture, or with natural or stained-wood trim or paneling. It sets a handsome and dignified tone in either home or office.

In addition to adding a vivid note to an interior these colors make telephoning more efficient because they make the telephone easy to see. They are pleasant because they can be so easily adapted to the accent color requirements of any type of room.

Since they became available to telephone subscribers on a national scale, more than ten million colored handsets have been sold at a price increase as high as ten dollars per set. The colored handsets have been a business asset for forward-looking and progressive organizations; their extensive and still increasing use by those organizations is yet another example of color's effect on a product's sales. Today there is a decided tendency for firms to create individuality and prestige in salesrooms, display rooms, and offices by using a co-ordinated color scheme. The colored telephone plays a big part in these merchandising programs. Telephone color has a functional use, too; one office uses red telephones for its direct lines and blue handsets for switchboard extensions.

132

Sales of colored telephones to date reflect the following preferences:

1. Ivory
2. Beige
3. Green
4. Red

5. Yellow
6. Blue
7. Gray
8. Brown

NEW COLOR IN PLACE OF NEW DESIGN

It is always worth while to enhance the visual value of a product through the skills of a qualified color engineer; with a change in color the product can be offered as an improved version. Redesign entails the heavy expense of tool and die changes while color change is a proven, sales-and-profit-producing, and less expensive step. Colors imparting a look of quality frequently overcome the natural sales resistance to the same product design clothed in a cheap and tawdry-looking finish coat of poorly selected and badly adapted colors. Even a quality product may be suffering from consumer neglect if it must fight the handicap of clumsy, ill-considered, and amateurish-looking color planning and selection.

There are, of course, a few qualifications to the use of new color as a sales tool. Up to a certain point, even a badly colored product's competitive position in the consumer market will improve as the product's price is lowered; there is, however, a portion of the market which will not buy poorly finished and colored merchandise regardless of price. On the other hand some color finishes and effects, while superior in sales appeal, are so expensive to apply that they increase cost beyond the point of marginal utility. Moreover, there are naturally some industries where product color is not a problem and cannot be used to improve market acceptance.

There is a new department in many manufacturing companies—its domain is "new products." Firm after firm has learned that there is need for diversification in its activities. In planning new products, the alert executive will take into account the fact that in today's market the area for product

133

improvement is limited when out-of-date colors are repeated year after year. But there are no such limits on new ways of using color to make products (old and new) impress prospects more favorably.

FACTORS IN PRODUCT–COLOR PLANNING

The entire field of color selection for products involves not only the study of psychology, but frequently the examination of the factual relationships covered by the sciences of physics, chemistry, psychophysics, physiology, and philosophy.

Take psychology. It is for psychological reasons that red is the color used to indicate high temperature or danger—red, since the time of primitive man, has been associated with heat and action in human thought and emotions. It is, on the other hand, for physical and physiological reasons that a yellow background is used to make black or dark threads more easily visible in some textile machines—the eye perceives more readily when bright yellow and black set each other off than when any other combination of colors is used.

Closely related to these psychological and physical considerations in planning color are those of color harmony and association. Both deal with individual reactions to color—we say colors are in harmony when, in the opinion of color-wise people, they enhance each other visually. In general, people appreciate happy color relationships; they sense when colors are right and when they are not.

Color association is another and even more individual reaction; we associate colors with certain occasions, events, purposes, or uses. A woman may like the color pink because of early flattery for her first pink dress. We associate good food with certain colors: how appetizing would be a piece of blue bread or a bright yellow steak? White is the color we associate with cleanliness: what would be the demand for a gray-looking sterile bandage and what effect would it have on the mental processes involved in healing?

134

Consumers' reactions to color—the dual reactions of harmony and association—vary widely on the basis of geography, age, sex, and time. A certain yellow once favored in the Southwestern United States as a bright and sunny color for room interiors was rejected in other regions as being too gaudy. A study made some years ago found that families of Italian extraction favored mother-of-pearl, tan, and blue-green for refrigerators; other national groups preferred different colors. As we discuss in greater detail in Chapter 8, color preference by car buyers shows a strong correlation with the country's economic condition: during bad times car buyers like the conservative and serviceable colors—black and dark shades; as times get better, brighter car colors move into the lead.

Color contrast is an important factor in product-color planning. One leading manufacturer of power saws introduced a new saw incorporating a color finish specifically designed to be distinctive from those of his competitors and to contrast well with an outdoor setting. Four major competitors had developed their color plans around orange, chrome yellow, royal blue, and stipple-finish gray, respectively. The manufacturer saw that eye-catching vermilion was distinctive and stood out well against the outdoor background. Coupling that color with a chrome finish on handles, guide bar, and chain provided color contrast, greatly improving safety and visibility.

Even fruit growers have a lesson to learn about the use of contrasting colors. A recent government survey indicates that shoppers favor apples that are half-red over fruit with less red color by a four-to-one margin. But, according to the same survey, sales drop off when the apples displayed are all red— an indication that shoppers are sold by the contrast in color.

Another example of the use of color contrast is my color plan for Cities Service Oil Company's pumps for its three grades of gasoline. At the time Cities Service brought out its new 100-octane fuel, other companies were also introducing new gasolines; one company planned to use a white pump for its premium gasoline, another a gold pump. The white was hard to see against snow and presented the printing problem of showing white against a white page in advertising, while the gold proved impossible to print in standard four-color advertising; it was excessively costly on the pumps and lacked both visual carrying power and uniform appearance under most types of illumination. I elected to use colors drawn from the previous pattern of high visibility and strong color compatibility that I had introduced to Cities Service pumps and stations some years before. The new pumps—dominantly red, yellow, and blue-green, respectively—maintained the high product identification of Cities Service colors, and contrasted equally well with backgrounds of white snow, the varying greens of foliage, and metropolitan gray. Yet they were perfectly compatible with each other under most natural and artificial light. All are high-visibility colors—yellow, for example, is used throughout the country on school buses, highway signs, and for airport marking—but they do not detract from each other and mutually enhance the selling power of the special fuels they designate, meeting today's increasing need for high-speed identification and recognition. A good color and design relationship is often more effective than a written message.

Color contrast is not always desirable, however. The strong contrast of some basic colors can slow factory production, in many cases, if applied to the work surfaces of factory machinery requiring close and constant supervision. Too strong basic colors, such as strong red and green or blue and orange, in powerful close contrast relationships tend to tire the eyes. Another example comes out of more of the experience of Cities Service. Some years ago the company realized that its antiquated-looking stations and spiritless black-and-white pumps were hurting sales. I suggested that red banding on a white pump for premium gas would stand out effectively if red were not introduced elsewhere on the station property. One official then raised the idea of achieving what he hoped would be still greater visibility and contrast by alternating stripes of the intense red and blue-green on the façade of the station. A large sheet of illustration board with the red and blue-green stripes painted directly alongside each other quickly demonstrated that the two neighboring basic colors created not high visibility but the disturbing flashing blur of a visual aberration.

Sometimes we have to reinterpret color tradition in the light of experiment. The result can be surprising. Take the case of the clothes that hunters wear to keep from going home strapped to the fender of some other and less perceptive hunter's car. Up until very recently these clothes were all red. That was tradition. Red was the color of danger and there are very few bright red animals or game birds. Some states even have laws that require hunters to wear red.

Not long ago, however, the National Rifle Association, the California Optometric Association, and the California Department of Fish and Game borrowed some soldiers from Fort Ord and sent them out into the woods to find out what colors made hunters most conspicuous. The answer? Yellow. Color-blind and non-color-blind personnel alike spotted yellow or a fluorescent orange long before they saw red.

Now at least one firm, the Saf-T-Bak Company in Altoona, Pennsylvania, is turning out hunting clothes in yellow. That manufacturer realizes that product-color decisions depend on a lot more than past practice or a good guess.

And while we're on the subject, hunters would gain an extra advantage if gun manufacturers would simply color the rear sights of guns yellow. The result would be greatly increased ease in aiming.

Another tradition was overcome with color to boost sales of Band-Aids. For years, Band-Aids were marketed in traditional, sanitary-looking, hospital white. The first color innovation was the appearance of flesh-colored Band-Aids, which are inconspicuous. After this camouflage job, however, came a really major change—colorful Band-Aids in assorted shapes and sizes with polka dots, stripes, and hearts in a rainbow of colors. As every parent knows, it's now impossible to keep a box of these new Band-Aids intact and away from children.

PRODUCT COLOR SHOULD BE DURABLE

In the selection of product colors it is essential not only that the colors selected should be suitable, but also that they be durable. One seldom sees purple or lilac-colored cars because these two colors, like certain others, tend to fade.

A good example comes from another of my research projects in determining practical color relationships. A previous chapter points out that Diesel locomotives are notably quiet, so quiet that people have been killed on the tracks because they did not hear a Diesel's approach. With this in mind the head of the Central Railroad of New Jersey asked me to develop a color plan for his line's Diesels which would be sufficiently conspicuous to help to overcome this danger hazard. The problem became one of determining what combination of pigments would produce the most distinctive and appropriate arrangement, and yet be economical from the standpoint of durability.

I found that ultramarine blue and orange made a distinctive combination with high and long-range visibility. A good strong orange was not hard to create, but the ultramarine blue proved impractical in a conventional lacquer vehicle because the acid action of nitrocellulose in the vehicle tended to break down the ultramarine pigment and turn it white. The eventual solution required the adoption of a synthetic finish containing an acid acceptor, the components of which did nothing to the detriment of the ultramarine. Later we introduced high-visibility colors to the equipment of many other types of transport carriers.

The durability of paint is not a matter of price. For the same color in finishes of comparable appearance there may be a price spread as great as 20 per cent. On the other hand, extremely durable Hansea yellow sells for approximately four times as much per pound as considerably less durable chrome yellow. Fortunately, with the guidance today of the directives and performance tests regarding pigments and vehicles established by the federal government, the color engineer can control the performance spread among different suppliers of finishes. During the war certain naval establishments found wide discrepancies in paint costs listed by various manufacturers; it was not until proper paint specifications were established against which bids were invited that the Navy was able to reduce the cost spread in its paint buying from 20 per cent to less than 5 per cent. Specification of ingredients, and performance tests, serve as protection against low-quality finishes. The price of these can be tempting but their serviceability will usually be brief.

HOW MANY COLORS?

A problem of approach faces the manufacturer who wants to apply the authority of the professional color engineer to increasing his sales. Should he use a few well-chosen basic colors or try to bring out his products in enough colors to meet any conceivable demand? There is a strong argument for the shotgun approach to choosing and manufacturing profitable color, and it finds a parallel in the restaurant business. When Howard Johnson went into this business he was in competition with experts, experts offering three flavors of ice cream: vanilla, chocolate, and strawberry. Vanilla was the big seller. Despite the advice of people who pointed out that obviously the public was buying vanilla because it wanted vanilla, Howard Johnson offered his customers twenty-six flavors of ice cream. His ice-cream sales were enormous but his sales of vanilla were small: clearly the public was buying vanilla because it had little other choice. The Howard Johnson method of offering the public whatever it might want turned into effective profit. Today, Howard Johnson restaurants feature twenty-eight flavors!

On the other hand a tile company tried a similar technique with tile color, featuring at one time a line of thirty-nine tile colors. Analysis showed that ten of these colors were constituting 79 per cent of the company's total sales. It certainly makes sense for a company faced with a similar situation to employ the authority and background of a color-engineering firm to select a practical line of colors. One of the situations where the experience and skill of a color engineer is most readily translated into profit is in the paring of elaborate and expensive color lines to the few colors that investigation and practical experience show the consumer will buy most readily.

HINTS ON COLOR AND DESIGN

When the progressive product designer goes to work he integrates his design with color. He does not design first and slap color on later. The design must be planned to take color planning gracefully and logically. This tight correlation of color and design has some vital effects.

First, color should fit logically into a section or sections of your product. Fussy and contrived-looking schemes are certainly never necessary, nor are color areas ending on a flat field without logical lines of demarcation. Where, for appearance or functional reasons, the designer wants to use color areas that do not follow the logical sections of the machine, he should create logical areas. A good example of this technique turns up in the automobile industry where chrome strips create areas for logical color placement on multicolored cars.

Second, material choice may have a determining effect on what colors you are going to be able to employ on your product. Different materials take color differently. Plastics are the best example; it is often difficult, for instance, to achieve a color match between two different plastic materials. The telephone colors I developed could not be matched in handsets with a phenolic handpiece and a butyrate base. The phenolic—albeit durable, inexpensive, and easy to mold—did not take well to color. The company then switched to an all-butyrate handset, only to find that this new material required different molding techniques and the eventual solution of some new acoustic difficulties. The company had an equally knotty problem integrating its rubber phone cords and metal dials into the new phones' eight basic color standards.

140

The lesson of this is that, with the diverse substances of modern industry, getting the color you want can often be expensive and sometimes impossible. This is another item of color preplanning that the designer should consider before he carries his appearance design concepts too far.

There should be pleasing visual unity between form and color.

The designer's object should be to give his product fewer, yet effective, colors and color relationships, colors that will be especially compatible with the maximum range of the product's end-use surroundings. It is in the selection of these correct colors that the designer finds himself increasingly dependent on the color engineer's close co-operation.

Color planning of products is an integral part of maintaining the visual identity or "corporate physiognomy" of any firm— the total impression that the company leaves with the consumer. An impression is established by an over-all color and design scheme as expressed in letterheads and bill forms in the appearance of factories and buildings, in the visual tone of reception rooms, in the container and label of a product, in the impact and tone of advertising and promotion, in the appearance of the truck that carries the product to market. When all of these factors are co-ordinated in colors that are sound and in keeping with the laws of good color and design planning, the total impact makes powerful sales and reorder insurance for any product.

WHERE DOES PRODUCT COLOR GO FROM HERE?

For twenty years I've been watching color move out of its backwater in the flow of industry and become a tool, a tool to increase effiicency, improve function, boost sales. I expect this increasing use and understanding of color will continue to grow. Here are some examples:

Automobiles. The new car colors will be softer and more

conservative in contrast to some of the gaudy combinations we've seen over the last few years. The dull depression favorites, colors of black and dark blue, gave way to a veritable rainbow of car finishes after World War II. Now these colors are being put to the test of the marketplace, and the consumer's dollar is making his color preference felt. Color there will be, but riot no longer. The drivers of the late 1950's will drive with more decorum, less dazzle.

Aircraft. The new passenger jets are on their way. They are shaping up at Boeing, Douglas, Lockheed, and Convair. It is a good bet that their high speeds and steep angles of descent will eventually require us to dress these jets in the same high-visibility colors the Navy and Air Force now prescribe for training planes and air-sea rescue craft. With traffic density still growing over our airports, exterior color is going to become an important factor in cutting the hazard of plane collision.

In their interiors, these planes will continue to use color to minimize the cigar shape of their fuselages and to create separate visual areas. They will also employ color to increase interior light reflectance. One of the current problems in commercial aircraft is the incongruous combination of near-sonic performance with model T lighting.

Home appliances. The color revolution in home appliances is already with us. In the future I think we can expect to see manufacturers color-planning their lines, not only for product-family compatibility but also for compatibility with the colorful homes of the future—with the bright new prefabricated homes now on the drawing boards and with the durable and colorful plastic interior-finishing materials we will use for our walls and ceilings in a few years.

Boats. In boats we will find the same increased use of color as a sales tool that we see in today's automobile industry. The man who buys a two-tone car is more than likely a sales prospect for a two-tone boat.

Farm and industrial machinery. Here, on the other hand, I feel functional color will supplant the present trend to using color for appearance or sales appeal. Color will highlight danger areas and flag hazards; it will abet ease of operation and both simplify and encourage maintenance. Strong, intense color on farm machinery enables the farmer to keep track of his equipment in the fields and to determine readily whether it is idle or in operation.

Office machines. With the trend toward attractive, modern color firmly established, I think we will again see an increased concentration of functional color—on such present problems as increasing keyboard legibility and differentiating various manual operations. Then, too, there will be an increasing trend toward matching color ensembles. Telephones, staplers, typewriters, will be in matching colors for each desk top. Ultimately, even desk tops may present a more colorful effect.

Over 40 per cent of all IBM electric typewriters are sold in color. Tan and green are the most popular.

Sixty per cent of all kitchens are now equipped with colored cabinets and appliances. Here again, color is proving most encouraging as a growth avenue.

Trains. Like aircraft, trains are being given the advantages of high-visibility color. In the future, I think we can expect to see trains continuing the trend toward high visibility and at the same time, using new and more durable finishes to build company personality—both on rolling stock and on the railroad's other equipment and structures and to reduce maintenance.

The Emerson Radio Corporation has advertised—and with reasonable pride—the fact that its line of colored plastic radios, radios embodying colors skillfully developed, increased sales 100 per cent. Every day, other manufacturers are finding similar results from the correct use of color. Color has too often been the stepchild of the industrial process. Product color, the *right* color, selected by the application of authoritative and experienced color engineering, is now opening a bright new field of profit to industry.

Luminaires—by Westinghouse—now come in alive-looking tan or green colors that spark extra sales, utility and décor excitement. The tan-colored fixture serves to help impart an accent of warmth. The green fixture is intended specifically to emphasize cool color schemes.

Needles lend themselves admirably to color engineering. Needles may be ideal from a design standpoint, but they are not good examples of functional color. Older people find it difficult to readily select small-eyed needles. Color-keying the thread end of the needle would prove a boon to sewers. A red-colored head should facilitate needle threading by providing better contrast for most thread colors.

COLOR COMMENTS

The U.S. Patent Office recently ordered new steel filing cabinets in solid color, instead of simulated wood finish—and saved the taxpayers $10,400.

Emily Post considers only blue, gray, and white stationery suitable for fastidious men and women.

The dash of color adds visual value. A slice of tomato, a sliver of pickle, a dash of shredded cabbage, makes a 60-cent sandwich look like a $1.25 lunch.

What happened to the multicolored money bill proposed by Representative Edith Nourse Rogers of Massachusetts? The currency of most foreign countries is denominated in accordance with a color schedule. The plan, except for the extra printing cost involved, would be a boon to all but the color-blind by readily identifying particular denominations by color. The extra cost involved in changing or increasing the color of currency would be an additional one-third. To provide a different color for each denomination would require eleven distinct variations.

The work of sorting peanuts on inspection lines at the Blakely Peanut Company was tough on eyes; they tired and smarted until the right shade of green was introduced on conveyor belts, manufactured by United States Rubber Company.

COLOR AND LIGHT IN THE MODERN OFFICE

Bernice Fitz-Gibbon, the New York career woman who knows her way around an office if anyone does, recently had this to say, in the *New York Times Magazine,* about her natural habitat:

The old gray lair ain't what it used to be. It ain't gray at all any more. The office these days has the equivalent—in spirit if not in fact—of yellow rubber tile floors, and limed pearwood woodwork, and Jens Risom desks, and Charles Eames chairs, and big-leafed chifaris in painted pots, blue or red telephones and chartreuse or beige typewriters....

The sun has set on the day of the dusty roll-topped desk, the bookkeeper's high stool, the green celluloid eye shade, and the concept of the office as a place where drudges are herded to eke out their livelihood in an atmosphere as convivial as that in a Renaissance crypt.

Miss Fitz-Gibbon attributes this latter-day decrypting of the office to the efforts of the army of woman employees which has infiltrated—nay, stormed—the fortresses of the nation's business over the last fifty years. Maybe so. I think the modern man has done much to minimize commercial murk on his

145

own. Whoever is responsible, it's becoming perfectly clear that the dingy and dank quarters of Scrooge and Marley are dead as the dodo. It's high time.

The modern office is a place where people work; color and light can do as much to build efficiency there as they can in the factory. Correct color and lighting can relax tension, improve morale, and stimulate action—they can cut down the bleak institutional atmosphere and convert the office to a comfortable and cheerful place to work. Once again, we run up against our standard problems. What colors? Which lights?

COLOR–PLANNING THE OFFICE

Office colors have to meet some stringent requirements. These are common-sense requirements—they don't depend on the caprice and whim of what the "decorator" thinks *looks* right. They depend, instead, on hard-headed considerations of efficiency and economy.

Office Colors Must Not Be Distracting

Distracting colors pull the worker's eye away from his work and leave him in the standard cartoon position of the stenographer: staring at a wall. The distracting colors are the strong-chroma ones; our offices' colors should be suitably subdued. Color, incidentally, can also compensate for existing distraction. In one company's New York office-showroom, orderly rows of dots in perforated wallboard disturbed several of the office's inhabitants. Color applied to the wallboard cleaned up the problem.

Office Colors Must Not Be Monotonous

This is the other side of the coin. Nondescript, neutral, lackluster colors can give your office the appealing cheerfulness of a peat bog. The trick, as the good football coach well knows, is mixing up your plays.

You can build a cheerful office personality by using the

146

functional color techniques we've already talked about. An alternation of warm and cool colors can break up an office's shape; a certain color can make a wall seem farther away from the worker's desk, another special color can make it seem closer. Stimulating colors will produce refreshing accents in areas not used as actual working spaces—corridors, storage bins, utility rooms, and entrance halls are a few such spaces.

One valuable resource the color engineer employs in his fight on monotony is the movable partition. I recently completed a color plan for the huge new Department of Defense building in Maryland. I developed a range of compatible colors for movable partitions, one color on one side, another color on the other. The building's occupants rearrange these partitions from time to time as their work requirements change; the variety of compatible colors permits them to create attractive, sprightly, and harmonious rooms as they will since the colors on the partitions are compatible with all of the other standards established for the rest of the building's décor. Thus the interior was divided by color screens to create an atmosphere of informality and privacy.

Office Colors Must Be Easy to Maintain

A lot of executives, knowing the high light-reflecting power of pastel colors, prescribe them for their company's offices. "Light colors," they say; "light and bright and save on the old electric bill." Alas, it spends on the old painting bill. Pastels do an admirable job of showing dirt. That means frequent washing and, with today's building-maintenance personnel what they so often are, frequent repainting.

The trick is to use a few colors properly, not a great many colors haphazardly—the rainbow office may or may not be an effective color plan, but it will be a most effective drain on your maintenance budget.

The most economical colors from the point of view of camouflaging dirt are certain cheery buffs, beiges, grayed greens and rose. Grays are also economical, but in using them you have to

147

watch out for the regrettable latterday tendency to hide dirt with colors which look dirty themselves.

One useful innovation we employ to beat the maintenance problem is painting the dado area of the lower wall in a deeper variation of the basic wall color; it is primarily this dado area which gets soiled.

Office Colors Must Promote Efficiency

You remember those psychological effects we discussed in our chapters on how to plan product colors and color in your factory. They work in the office, too. If your office is too warm, turn down the heat. If it's *still* too warm, paint it in the cool colors, the pastel blues and blue-greens. If your office is gloomy or foreboding or just plain dull, paint it with creams, tans, yellow-greens, pinks, or golden beiges—these are the colors that stimulate and promote well-being. If it's *too* stimulated, a soothing turquoise is prescribed.

GIVE THE EMPLOYEES A SAY

The Navy lets its ship skippers pick interior colors from a range of carefully selected options. Why don't you give your *crew* some say? A lot of money and a lot of time and several cubic feet of typescript have gone into studies by social scientists on how to improve worker morale. There's a handy way to do it with the nearest telephone. Order a palette of professionally engineered colors—the color engineer can develop for you eight or ten colors which will meet the requirements set out in our last section and be compatible with each other. Then turn your employees loose and let them pick among these colors as they will. You'll find that they develop a housekeeping interest in your business that you hardly would have thought possible. Listen to what D. F. Edwards, General Superintendent of Esso's Bayonne refinery, has to say about this:

The color program has been used to increase employee interest and *esprit de corps* through participation. When planning the renovation of an office or shop, we have made a practice of consulting the people working in the area. We ask them to choose color schemes and make other suggestions. The end result is arrived at by group participation. We . . . feel we have obtained a tremendous amount of employee satisfaction and a feeling of participation, of "being on the team."

SEVEN VARIED OFFICE COLOR PLANS *

WALLS	RUG	UPHOLSTERY	DRAPERIES
1. 3 Oyster White, 1 light Brick Red	Silver Gray	Light Brick Red	Gray plaid with metallic silver thread running through it
2. Lemon Yellow	Cork Tan	Natural pigskin	Heather mixture in shades of Gold, Tan, Brown
3. Light Violet-Blue, somewhat grayed	Sepia Brown	Royal Blue leather	Tan and Brown tweed texture
4. 3 light Gray-Green, 1 Forest Green	Very light Gray	Bright Red-Orange	White
5. Turquoise, slightly grayed and medium light	Rust Red	Turquoise, darker than wall	Brown, Rust and Turquoise plaid or heather mixture
6. 3 Silver Gray, 1 medium Emerald Green	Royal Blue	Emerald Green leather and Vermilion leather	Royal Blue
7. Light Beaver Tan	Dark Green	Chartreuse and Beaver Tan leather	Chartreuse

* This color range includes something appropriate from every color family except purple. This assortment should provide a color menu with sufficient choice to meet every taste.

NOT JUST PAINT

Color in your office need not stop with the paint brush. Go look at a display of the colorful new office equipment, of the typewriters, staplers, and adding machines, and you can see that for yourself.

Office equipment is breaking out in a veritable kaleidoscope of color. Time was when the ubiquitous stapler, for example, was chrome-plated, giving it the pleasant and homelike attractiveness of a surgical saw. No more. Take the staplers we color-planned for the Bates Manufacturing Company. They now come in color with bright and cheerful plastic knobs in red, blue, and yellow. Not only do our new Bates colors make the staplers more cheerful; they also have a unique functional effect—they keep staplers from walking over to another desk. When an office girl has a stapler with a yellow knob she develops a feeling of ownership. Instead of demanding a new stapler when hers goes astray, she sets out to get it back.

By and large there is plenty of room for future development in office-equipment color. Most of today's office machines come in crackled or crystalline finishes, many of which, regrettably, are dust catchers. Two-tone spatter finishes, hammered metal, and finishes simulating hammered metals, lacquers embodying fine metal flakes—all of these are fertile fields for office color innovation.

There is still room for new office color co-ordination.

Air conditioners inject their currently hideous posteriors into many offices; there's no reason in the world why the air conditioner cannot be made an attractive piece of equipment through color.

Desk tops are still too often a dull black or a dark brown, setting up a painful contrast in the eye of the worker confronted with a snowdrift of white paper. Light-colored desk tops can solve this problem.

Office furniture tends to be humdrum. Color planning can give your office furniture a personality friendly to that color

150

personality you build into your office. The modern and progressive office-furniture manufacturer ought to be thinking about clothing his wares in a few fast-selling compatible colors which will join with and enhance any modern office color plan.

Filing cabinets loom up in a colorless array like a line of rampant hippopotamuses. These cabinets used to be olive drab or an imitation mahogany; now they're most often gray. Unnecessary gloom, that. Again, more progressive manufacturers ought to do something about it, introducing at least two compatible colors in their lines.

IT'S TIME OFFICES SAW THE LIGHT

Office work is eye work. Is your office easy on the eyes? If it isn't you're losing work, reducing morale, and probably having trouble keeping your employees and gaining new ones. Correct illumination can be a crucial factor in making your office a better and more efficient place to work in.

Time was when you called in an electrician and said, "Put a light over there." You got a light. Some time afterward, you got a headache. Illumination planning is like tightrope walking—it takes some delicate balancing and it's no job for the amateur.

The first problem that the illumination engineer faces when he designs a lighting installation for an office is *how much light?* Illumination levels in most offices are too low for truly efficient eye work. Engineers walk around with light meters measuring lighting levels in *foot-candles*—a foot-candle is the amount of light thrown onto a square foot of surface one foot away from an *international candle*, a sperm candle of a certain diameter burning at a certain rate.

In our work in developing office illumination here are the foot-candle levels we try to attain. Estimates are for minimum foot-candles thirty inches above the floor.

For Most Difficult Seeing Tasks—100 or more foot-candles.
This is finest precision work involving finest detail, poor con-

trasts, and long periods of time, such as drafting, designing, color matching.

For Very Difficult Seeing Tasks—100 foot-candles.

This is precision work involving fine detail, fair contrasts, and long periods of time, such as tabulating, auditing, bookkeeping.

For Difficult and Critical Seeing Tasks—50 foot-candles.

This is prolonged work involving fine detail, moderate contrasts, and long periods of time, such as business machine operation, filing, cataloguing.

For Ordinary Seeing Tasks—40 foot-candles.

This is for work involving moderately fine detail, normal contrasts, and intermittent periods of time, such as work done in general offices, laboratories, conference rooms, mail rooms.

For Casual Seeing Tasks—30 foot-candles.

This involves such locations as stairways, receptions rooms, washrooms and other service areas, active storage.

For Rough Seeing Tasks—20 foot-candles.

This involves such locations as hallways, corridors, passageways, inactive storage.

Building some fixtures which will pump out enough foot-candles of light isn't the whole story, however. The second problem is making sure that your new light doesn't produce harmful contrasts. This involves the study of brightness contrast. We don't want too much contrast between the lighting fixture and its surroundings and the worker's work and *its* surroundings. The best ratio is roughly three to one—the fixture three times as bright as its ceiling; the work three times as bright as its adjacent area.

Overhead we achieve this brightness contrast by diffusing the light from the fixture and letting it bounce back up on the ceiling or by making the entire ceiling a lighting fixture. On the area surrounding the worker's work we use high-reflectance colors—still another example of the hand-in-hand relationship of color and light. Most officers stray discouragingly from this

152

three-to-one ratio. We worked on one office where there was a *sixty-to-one* contrast ratio; when we cut the ratio to three to one, errors dropped 12 per cent.

Many types of fixtures smooth out this ratio and at the same time carry on the important related job of cutting down the harmful contrast bred by heavy shadows. Let's look at some of the more recent types of fixtures which my organization has found useful:

The louverall ceiling. This installation employs acrylic plastic louvers suspended below rows of lamps; it gives good downward lighting punch and excellent diffusion, and is readily susceptible to the type of color correction we discussed in our section on supermarket lighting. The louverall ceiling does an especially good job of eliminating shadows by permitting the use of very intense light. The louverall installation by which we modernized the office of Mr. William C. Newberg, Chrysler Executive Vice-President, increased the light level from 29 foot-candles to 58 foot-candles. This improvement has brought requests for the same optimum lighting in offices of other Detroit executives.

The troffer system. A troffer is the common (usually rectangular) fixture with parallel fluorescent tubes that hangs from the ceiling or is recessed into it. In using troffers it is essential that we take care to keep the reflectance of the surrounding ceiling high—otherwise our brightness-contrast ratio may get out of hand. The best way to arrange troffers to minimize shadows is in a crisscross pattern, not in the parallel rows we find in so many offices.

The trolley system. This system provides mobile lamps in Bulldog Trolley ducts so the lamps can be moved around. Developed for supermarkets, the trolley system would work equally well in any office where light-level requirements vary —a design office, for example, or an advertising agency's art department.

Indirect lighting. The term indirect lighting covers a multitude of installations, but there is a special type of indirect lighting which bodes well for the future. This ties the fluorescent lamp into the movable partition, that great and recent boon to the shifting layout requirements of the modern office. Fluorescent lamps can be incorporated in coves built into the top of these movable partitions—when they move the light goes with them. The lamps throw their light against the office ceiling. With a well-engineered installation this form of indirect lighting can eliminate the necessity for desk lamps entirely.

Another lighting system which shows extreme promise for office illumination is Westinghouse's electroluminescent system. Using glass panels containing embedded phosphor powers, the system changes its panel's color by varying the character of an electric current which energizes the panels. Westinghouse has demonstrated panels which change from blue to green to orange to red with a flick of a switch. The light is shadowless and bright, and its intensity is easy to control. If Westinghouse adopts proper and effective colors for its production panels, electroluminescence looms as a possible office light of the not-too-distant future.

LIGHT ON OFFICE COLOR

So much for lighting in the abstract. In practice, no matter how much light your lighting installation pumps out, its efficiency is going to depend on color. So we have come full circle. We've already discussed some of the characteristics that we need in office color. Now let's look at the rest of those characteristics—at the characteristics that specifically depend on light.

Office Colors Must Have High Reflectance

Too many office colors soak up light; I recently color-planned and relighted an office which was afflicting its workers with an illumination level approximating that of moonlight.

You'll find it useful, in considering light reflectance, to refer

154

back to the reflectance table (page 106) in our chapter on color in your factory. It is just as valid for the office as it was for the factory.

The colors with the highest reflectance, of course, give you the most light for a given illumination installation. If you paint your office all white, you will get lots of light—but it will be so dazzling that you will find it as eye-soothing as a sunny day on the Greenland icecap. You can avoid this dazzle by following nature's rule of greatest light overhead, medium light in the middle reaches, and least light underfoot. A good rule of thumb is:

SURFACE	REFLECTANCE (PER CENT)
Ceiling	83–75
Upper walls	50
Lower walls	35
Desk tops	40
Flooring	10

The right flat or semigloss finish colors can give a good level of reflectance if there is adequate illumination. Ceilings should be painted in high-reflectance versions of these colors; doors, door frames, dado, and baseboards in lower reflectance values, the same color families, and preferably dull-finish enamel. The floor can be either similar or contrasting to the wall color.

The Kinds of Light and Color

Office colors must be developed with regard to present or planned types of illumination. Colors change appearance under different lights. The co-ordination of color and light can be important in developing office décor.

Artificial office lighting depends chiefly on incandescent or fluorescent lamps. Fluorescent fixtures emit four kinds of light, called Warmtone Deluxe White, Warmtone White, Daylight, and Deluxe Cool White. Thus five principal kinds of light are available, and of the five the incandescent and the Deluxe Cool White are the most diverse in their effect on color.

155

The principal color-groupings are: warm colors, cold colors, medium colors, and neutrals.

Let's mix up colors and light sources and see what comes out.

Warm colors. The colors on the warm side of the spectrum—including red, maroon, wine, orange, golden yellow, pink, rust, peach, tan, beige, and brown—look deeper and richer under incandescent light than they do in natural daylight; they also take on a slightly brownish cast.

Under Deluxe Cool White they look clearer and brighter and avoid the brownish cast. On the other hand they lose the depth that incandescent light gives them.

Cold colors. The cold colors on the other side of the spectrum—colors such as the blue-greens, the true blues, and the violet-blues—take on a slightly greenish hue under incandescent light. Under Deluxe Cool White they pick up a very slight violet tinge but otherwise appear natural and unchanged.

Medium colors. Between the warm and cool sides of the spectrum lie the true greens. They tend to appear yellower under incandescent light and bluer under Deluxe Cool White. Dark green looks olive under incandescent light. Chartreuse looks yellower under incandescent light and appears almost pure green under Deluxe Cool White.

Neutral colors. The neutrals range from black through myriad grays to white. Since true neutral grays exhibit no chroma of their own they take on different hues under the five kinds of light, varying from slightly reddish under incandescent to slightly bluish under Deluxe Cool White. The chart shows what happens to them under our different light sources.

TYPE OF LIGHT	APPEARANCE OF NEUTRAL COLORS
Incandescent	Slightly red
Warmtone Deluxe White	Slightly orange
Warmtone White	Slightly yellow
Daylight (fluorescent)	Slightly green
Deluxe Cool White	Slightly blue

Unless we consider these effects, we can try to employ all the functional features of color we've talked about in the rest of this chapter and find that they just don't work. It takes the experience that goes with long years of color engineering to sift through and sort out these effects, and to apply them to the tough and important job of making your office a better and more profitable place to work.

COLOR: KEY TO SUCCESSFUL ADVERTISING

You may never have seen a purple cow but you may have seen a green horse—in a Smirnoff Vodka ad not too long ago. The story of the green horse and how he got that way is a capsule story of some of the problems color raises in advertising.

The emerald equine was the brainhorse of the Lawrence C. Gumbinner Advertising Agency, who advertise Smirnoff's. That agency had been using color in the Smirnoff ads for its shock effect; the agency's Art Director, Hershel Bramson, thought a green horse on a yellow beach would be a specially effective shocker.

Its first job was finding a horse—photographer Bert Stern turned up a suitably photogenic one in a New York riding stable. Its next problem was to turn the horse green. For this somewhat more complex job the photographer called on a stage make-up expert; the expert, an old Ziegfeld Follies man, had had no experience with developing suitable tints for a horse complexion but he came forward with a pail full of green paint which he felt would cover the problem.

The photographer and his assistant proceeded to daub this

158

paint on the horse. The job proceeded with growing difficulty as the horse's attitude changed from tolerant interest to outright concern. Finally the horse was green and the photographer stood back to view his handiwork.

It was bad—the horse clearly lacked allure. On the other hand, it was also late—the picture had to be shot that day and accordingly the photographer bundled the horse into an open trailer and set out for a suitably photogenic beach, hoping neither the horse nor his complexion would run before they got there.

As he drove down Brooklyn's Flatbush Avenue it became apparent to the photographer that this hope was optimistic. He was stopped five times by other cars, each time to learn that he was towing a horse showing manifest exterior signs of extreme illness.

By the time the caravan arrived at the beach the horse was sweating like a horse, either from the heat or embarrassment. What made this sweating more discouraging was that it was clearly modifying the horse's hue. Unable to change horses in mid-beach, the photographer shot his pictures anyway, returned the horse to its owner who promptly put it to bed to ease its shock, and then took to his bed himself, first dosing himself with a fifth of the account's product.

When the color transparencies came through, the photographer was astounded to find that the horse knew what he had been up to after all. The faded green was just what he had been trying to get all along; the ad was eminently successful and the horse was last seen auditioning for the Mobilgas account.

The moral of all this is that color advertising can be difficult, expensive, time-consuming, and sometimes downright discouraging. But as Smirnoff, Gumbinner, the photographer, and the horse would all testify, correct advertising color correctly used pays and pays well.

ADVERTISING COLOR BRINGS 'EM IN

The right colors in an advertisement can command extraordinary attention and turn in a vastly superior selling job compared to the conventional ad in black-and-white.

Let's look at the examples:

A national advertisement in full color produced $250,000 in sales; the same ad in black-and-white brought in $80,000.

A large mail-order apparel house used two illustrations of the same dress in its catalogue, one in color and the other in black-and-white. On separate pages and identified with different order numbers, the color ad pulled in more than eight times as many orders as the black-and-white one.

A seed merchant switched his flower catalogue from black-and-white to color and watched his orders climb more than 900 per cent.

Another seed company ran color ads in several trade magazines catering to the canning industry—so far as it knows, the first four-color ads used in such magazines. The ads featured four items, two of which sold out completely. The company received one order for a ton of bean seeds clipped to one of the ad's superb color photographs.

An advertising agency surveyed readers for a shaving-cream account, finding that 25 per cent of one publication's readers remembered the account's ad when it was in two colors while only 8 per cent remembered it in black-and-white.

A similar survey found that a baking-powder manufacturer's full-color ad stopped 77 per cent of a publication's readers, while the same ad in black-and-white stopped only 19 per cent.

A Starch survey of 1,026 consumer-magazine advertisements showed that color ads, on an average, produce 50 per cent greater readership than black-and-white ads. Women, for example, were least interested in automobiles. Yet where color was included in the ad, readership was 130 per cent greater than for black-and-white.

160

ALL ADVERTISING COLOR ISN'T GOOD

With results like those we've just seen it looks as if advertising agencies would be scrambling for professional help in developing colors which take advantage of color's proven selling power. Too often this hasn't been the case, and a thumb-through of a couple of current national magazines will show it.

Here are some of the advertising color calamities I found in issues of *Life* and the *Saturday Evening Post*.

In a Ford ad a comparatively colorless blue-and-white car appears in front of a colorful red, black, yellow, and white cruise ship. The ship is clearly outstanding; if you're in the business of selling luxury liners, this ad is tailor-made for you.

A Webcor phonograph advertisement combines an all-over bright orange plate with black-and-white; the orange is a strident and discordant color with no musical associations.

An advertisement for Spud cigarettes features a picture of the product's new pack against a white background. Because of this white background the ad is forced to gray the white in the pack, destroying the visual identify of the ad's pack with packs of Spuds on the shelf.

A two-page ad for S. & W. Green Trading Stamps hides the stamps amidst a profusion of colored trade-marks and bright artwork, all competing for the eye's attention. Several members of my staff read the same issue I did. All of them remembered the ad but not one remembered what it was advertising.

An ad for Du Pont cellophane shows a mother putting a pack of cellophane-wrapped sandwiches in her boy's knapsack. The thesis of the ad is that "Bread's at Its Best in Cellophane" and the ad, one assumes, is designed to capitalize on the appetizing appearance of the sandwich when wrapped in cellophane. Regrettably the knapsack, the mother's sweater, and the sandwiches' lettuce appear in a thoroughly nonappetizing shade of green, nearly an olive drab. Green can be one of the most appetizing colors but Du Pont's green in this ad effectively loses that valuable color association.

161

This is no general indictment of color advertising. Some of it is topnotch. In the same magazines containing these misuses of advertising colors I find for example, a delightful Life Saver advertisement listing the disagreeable food aftertastes that Life Savers presumably counteract. The names of foods are in paled, unappetizing colors; the Life Saver package, on the other hand, stands out in its refreshing and cool blue. This is color used well. The problem: how to score a color home run like this every time you come to bat.

THE NINE RULES
OF COLOR IN ADVERTISING

In my own experience with developing colors for advertising I've formulated nine rules. These are not self-evident rules nor are they created out of the blue. They are rules based on more than twenty years of experience with hard-headed business problems of which ads sell and which don't.

1. *Use logical and appropriate colors.* This is a return to the psychological impact of color we've already talked about. Some colors have certain associations. These associations must be exploited to help your ad sell what it's supposed to sell. Suppose you're selling "hot food." If you set up those words in a bluish-green ink, you're running headlong into the cool associations people have with this color. Bluish greens set up a subconscious reaction of cold; your ad's impact is nullified by this reaction.

2. *Use attention-getting colors.* This means, nowadays, unusual colors and color combinations. Look at the neon signs lining your main street the next time you go out at night. Out of the miles of stores advertising themselves with red neon signs ("Aha," said the store owner, "I want attention, so I'll use red!"), the neon signs you'll notice will be ones in some other color. Exactly the same phenomenon holds true for advertising.

3. *Use legible colors.* An important part of your advertising message will be carried by text. If you use colors which make the

text hard to read, it won't get read. Be careful to avoid too many type faces and colors in carrying out this job and watch out for large areas of drop-out color plates—they're painfully hard to read.

4. *Use consistent colors.* Color can build a unified personality for your business—for your stores, products, packages, vehicles, *and* your advertising. This sort of unified personality will build your readership and increase the recall ability of that readership. The good series of advertisements will show a consistent and highly personal color plan.

5. *Use colors that satisfy current wants.* Consumer color preferences back and fill with the changes in the country's economic condition. Get professional help in keeping track of these color-preference changes and then develop your advertisements so they feature the colors that people want.

6. *Use logical color consideration in deciding on photography or artwork.* If the product you want to advertise meets all the color considerations we've talked about and is photogenic to boot, photographs are probably your best bet. If your product doesn't lend itself to effective color reproduction, you'll do better with artwork.

7. *Pretest your color reproduction.* An ingenious tool for pretesting advertising color has recently gone on the market. Called the Coloron and a product of the Delta Brush Manufacturing Company in New York, it consists of a set of twelve transparent sheets—in eleven colors and black—printed with a series of panels graduated from a 10 per cent tint to a solid panel of the sheet's color. Each sheet also shows different uses of type in the sheet's color: surprint, dropout, tinted on solid ink, tinted on stock. The sheets come in the four-color process colors plus red, yellow, blue, green, orange, purple, and brown; the tints are 110-line screen. By shuffling the Coloron's panels you can handily duplicate the colors you'll obtain by a similar concatenation of printing plates. Delta also makes a Coloron for halftones. Both are invaluable tools in deciding how your color work will reproduce.

8. *Check your colors carefully once you have them developed.* A fine color program can come a cropper through bad reproduction. In checking progressive proofs make sure you have the proper light, that you match proof and copy, and that plates register properly. A handsome Italian Line advertisement in a national publication failed to register properly; the result was not a flood of prospective tourists but a flood of perplexed readers.

9. *Don't lose sight of color's advertising advantages in publications other than magazines.* Newspaper color is a good example. Run-of-paper color has grown enormously in importance. Almost all metropolitan newspapers in the United States offer some kind of ROP color. The big problem with ROP color is that it sometimes goes aground on technical limitations; there are few newspapers, for example, in which it is safe to schedule an ROP halftone. The trick in ROP color is developing simple, sprightly, basic colors which will be at home in the bright, alert setting of a newspaper. Of course these colors must be used so that registration is not important; registration, as yet, is not the forte of the ROP color press. But a recent Starch survey showed that ROP color ads, as opposed to black-and-white, were noted by 71 per cent more men and 23 per cent more women; they were read most by 25 per cent more men and 53 per cent more women.

Color advertising runs into money. A four-color page in the *Saturday Evening Post* cost, in 1958, in the neighborhood of $27,000. In *Life* Magazine a color page in 1957 could set you back as much as $42,000. A year's run of a four-color page a week, in these terms, becomes a more than million-dollar investment—big money in anybody's business. This expense is justified only if color is used at its forced-draft effect; otherwise it just isn't worth the money. With the cost of advertising color what it is, the agency which fails to employ all the modern tools at the disposal of the color engineer is being penny-wise and pound-foolish. The advertiser who capitalizes on correct color

164

will find that pound-wise means color-wise in advertising. Above all, he should never permit color to contradict a desired impression.

THE VALUES OF COLOR IN PRINTING

Occasionally a printer is asked if, in his opinion, the use of color in printing increases results. To answer this question truthfully, he can say that the experience of larger users of printing, such as the mail-order houses, claim there is no doubt about it. Certainly the use of color stimulates returns. Color will catch the eye where black-and-white may fail.

Merely to use color for the sake of color is perhaps not enough; color should be put to work where, used simply and appropriately, it will invite readership. Color must be handled with care for there is nothing more disturbing than a piece of printing with too much color, which sometimes defeats its own purpose. Psychologists point out that because of the many curious mental and emotional associations of color, subtle applications are possible. The real test, of course, is the end result; that is, that printed pieces using color get better results.

A New York publisher printed a very fine edition of a book and a large sale was anticipated. The book was bound in good-quality red cloth, with gilt top and rough edges, but the publisher made the mistake of using a one-color jacket. The book did not sell and the publisher was left with a large quantity of books.

Realizing that something must be done, it was decided to use a more colorful jacket. A well-known artist was employed to paint a picture in full color and this was used on the jacket, the frontispiece and the cover insert. The first books were recalled and the book republished. Instantly the sales picked up and the entire edition was sold out. The publisher learned that color will sell books and since that time, this type of jacket has become the pattern for a whole series.

COLOR COMMENTS

Sign builders should become more efficient, more skillful and more resourceful in helping their clients in the successful utilization of sign advertising. Above all, they need to give the public credit for good taste and intelligence.

Sign advertising had its origin at the ball park. A large white building directly in line with the batter's line of vision camouflaged the white baseball. Some enterprising soul painted the façade of the building black to provide contrast. This in turn suggested using that prominent space for the first display advertising.

The following color groupings will be most striking shown, in the order named, against black backgrounds.

Light Red and dark Red
Pink and Magenta Pink
Light Orange and Tan
Pale and deep Yellow
Light Yellow-Green and Olive
Light and dark Violet-Blue
Sky Blue and Indigo
Lavender and Purple

HOW TO GET YOUR ADVERTISING READY
FOR COLOR TV

Color television has been having teething troubles, born of electronic complexity, programming problems, and some unexpected sales resistance. Those antediluvians who can remember back to the flickering yellow-green screens of the late 1940's may recall that what was even then called black-and-white TV faced a similar set of pediatric diseases but recovered nicely. Color TV is with us, it is expanding, and nobody in the industry seriously doubts that it will some day—in two or five or ten years—largely supplant black-and-white. Tagging right along with the growth of color TV is a ferocious set of color problems; no matter when color TV will take over the market, advertisers had better start worrying about these basic problems right now.

The electronic processes peculiar to color TV do some remarkable things to color:

Red bleeds through into other colors (blue areas, especially), particularly in outdoor scenes. This makes blue tones tend to look purplish.

Yellow shows up light. It is therefore necessary to use darker yellows to simulate lighter yellows in most cases.

167

Deep, dark reds are similarly ineffective.

Neutral gray is badly distorted, especially if the home receiver is out of adjustment.

Grayed or pastel colors show up brighter and more intensely on the color TV screen than they do in the studio.

These effects can have some appalling results on product color, as *Sponsor* Magazine pointed out in a recent issue. Preserves turn black; white paint becomes gray; copperware looks like silver; beer labels show up black; shrimp reproduces so white it looks unreal. Margarine looks like ice cream and rice comes out appearing dirty. Silverware produces a scintillating series of black blurs and necktie colors darken against light shirts.

These are just a few of the color problems you face when you bring your advertising program into the color TV studio. Even when you apply the color engineer's knowledge of the workings of color to specific applications of color in TV advertising, the complexity boggles the mind.

COLOR TV AND MAKE-UP

Despite a latter-day trend to employing cartoon characters, animated fish, and ambulatory beer bottles as salesmen for your product, much of today's TV advertising relies on people—filmed or live—to do its selling. This emphasis on the electronic version of our old friend the pitchman causes serious color problems: although the viewer may not care if Betty Beauty's dress is green instead of pink, he will be deeply concerned if her face is.

Stage make-up generally won't work on color TV. The stage requires high coloring while subdued tones reproduce best through the TV camera. Even these subdued tones will pick up color casts from clothes, and one of the most important problems the TV advertiser faces is the overlapping of clothes and complexion.

168

Here are some of the clothing-color considerations for the various complexion types as they appear on color TV:

Redheads—Medium neutral gray and light gray make them look more vivid; rust gives less appeal; yellow-green adversely affects the redhead's complexion. Faded pinks are splendid.

Brunettes—Medium neutral gray or bright dark blue makes them look more vivid; light gray gives a tanned look; yellow brings out the pinkish tones in brunettes.

Blondes—Medium neutral gray makes them look faded; light gray gives them a darker look; medium tan or bright dark blue adds vividness; yellow gives blondes a violet cast.

White Hair—Medium neutral gray or light gray makes skin coloring of women with white hair look faded; yellow gives a violet cast; light violet-blue brings out fresh pinkish tones; bright dark blue makes these people look sallow.

COLOR TV AND FABRIC COLORS

Closely related to the make-up problem is that of clothing fabrics. Fabric colors whirl around in TV's electronic environment and come out changed. Take that everyday stand-by of the American male, the ubiquitous white shirt. White is too much for today's color systems. It appears much too bright on the receiver. It takes a gray or blue shirt with one-half the reflectivity of white to look like a white shirt on color TV.

A good basic rule in costuming for color TV is always to avoid white for large areas. Today's video equipment will gag on a picture with more than 20 per cent of its area in white. Norman Grant, one of the bright designers who have been pioneering TV work, has another sound basic rule: avoid color extremes and very sharp contrasts.

A related problem is color saturation. Consider a red shirtwaist against a blue background. The variation of brightness between red and blue will diffuse the transition between figure and ground and the edges of the waist will appear to smear. It

169

takes a substitution of yellow for red and a change in brightness of the background to make the color transition effective.

COLOR TV AND PACKAGE COLORS

The advent of color TV has complicated the problems of window display and package design to say nothing of product presentation in general because of the effect of lighting on the color scheme of a scene.

In our section on packaging, we saw how your package is not only the last-chance salesman of your product but often the most effective one. We found that packages have to be adaptable—that their selling environment requires them to look at home and to work effectively on the shelves of a supermarket, in the display case of the corner candy store, or in the pages of an advertisement.

Color TV puts the package in still another selling environment, and a tough one it is indeed. Not only do all the color phenomena occur that we saw in our packaging chapter, but the package's colors may not occur at all. This poses the first tough problem for the packager. Should he shoot for a package which will look the same at its point of sale or on the color TV screen, or shall he knuckle under to TV's tricks and show viewers a package which *they* think looks like the one in the supermarket but which in fact may look very different?

There is no pat solution. All we can do is list the factors which will influence your decision:

1. It is difficult and sometimes costly to develop package colors which will look the same on color and black-and-white TV and "in the flesh."

2. Such a redesign may lose the selling value of your carefully established present package colors.

3. On the other hand, more and more advertising is originating from the point of sale; if your package is unrecognizable when the camera moves into that supermarket, it has become a very expensive package indeed.

170

4. Using special colors which simulate your package on TV may or may not produce a convincing replica.

As a rule of thumb, you will probably fare best if you make a brand-new package line compatible with black-and-white or color and point-of-sale viewing, a complex job best left in the hands of the color engineer. If you are retaining your old package line, the problems of making it compatible may be insurmountable, and you had better get professional help in trying to simulate your package on TV as closely as possible.

COLOR AND LIGHTING ON TV

Lighting has an immense job to do with getting your advertising message over to the viewer. Lighting can make or break TV colors; it is even more important than lighting for black-and-white. Lighting for color TV must be comparatively shadowless and extremely bright—the average level of light on a color TV set runs four to six times that of black-and-white. If the originating studio doesn't have color-controlled and color-integrated lighting, for example, small objects with slight color differences—like people's faces—will show up poorly.

The lighting of a studio, if it is carefully co-ordinated, can do a much better job of presenting your advertising message than natural lighting. The big problem is co-ordinating that lighting with the colors you want to transmit.

The color engineer handles this with a color-and-light correlation chart. Such a chart gives information on the typical color of the conventional studio light sources, the color of the pigment that the light will reflect from, the resultant hue, and whether the value and chroma of the pigment are respectively raised or lowered and strengthened or weakened. The chart illustrates the results that can be expected from various typical surface textures. You will note that the term "value" given in Appendix C represents dimension of lightness or darkness of a color while "chroma" is the attribute of purity or strength in a color.

Here is a typical light-correlation chart. Of course, in work-

171

aday practice the color engineer is concerned with a vastly greater number of pigments and light colors.

LIGHT CORRELATION CHART

COLOR OF LIGHT	COLOR OF PIGMENT	RESULTANT HUE	VALUE	CHROMA
Red	Red	Unchanged	Raised	Unchanged
	Yellow	Yellow-Red	Raised	Unchanged
	Green	Brownish Gray	Raised	Unchanged
	Blue	Reddish Gray	Lowered	Unchanged
	Purple	Imparts Yellow-Red	Raised	Strengthened
Yellow	Red	Yellow-Red	Raised	Unchanged
	Yellow	Yellow	Unchanged	Unchanged
	Green	Yellow-Green-Yellow	Raised	Weakened
	Blue	Grayed Yellow	Lowered	Strengthened
	Purple	Brownish	Lowered	Weakened
Green	Red	Brownish Gray	Lowered	Weakened
	Yellow	Lemonish Yellow	Raised	Weakened
	Green	Neutral Green	Unchanged	Unchanged
	Blue	Bluish Green	Unchanged	Weakened
	Purple	Grayish Brown	Unchanged	Weakened
Blue	Red	Reddish Purple	Unchanged	Weakened
	Yellow	Neutralized	Unchanged	Weakened
	Green	Blue-Green	Unchanged	Weakened
	Blue	Unchanged	Unchanged	Strengthened
	Purple	Grayed	Lowered	Weakened
Violet	Red	Bluish	Lowered	Unchanged
	Yellow	Neutralized	Lowered	Unchanged
	Green	Violet-Gray	Lowered	Weakened
	Blue	Slate Blue	Lowered	Weakened
	Purple	Purple	Raised	Strengthened
Purple	Red	Bluish	Unchanged	Unchanged
	Yellow	Grayed	Lowered	Weakened
	Green	Grayed	Lowered	Weakened
	Blue	Blue-Gray	Unchanged	Unchanged
	Purple	Unchanged	Lowered	Unchanged

COMPATIBLE COLOR:
THE TV PROBLEM IS COMPOUNDED

As color TV pokes its head over the horizon, black-and-white is firmly established. The disturbing thing about this lackluster if somewhat larger member of the communications industry is that black-and-white TV, paradoxically enough, spawns a host of color problems on its own.

Strange as it may seem, the plain old black-and-white days of the remote Milton Berle–Jerry Lester–Wendy Barrie era had their color troubles. Black costumes ringed actors with fire; sequins produced a halo around their wearer. Lucky Strike's black lettering merged into its red bull's-eye; Old Gold's yellow-red lettering disappeared against its yellow background.

As a result, some strange colors appeared before the TV camera. For a time there was a movement toward staging all black-and-white TV in tones of gray or sepia, but the grays lost the live quality which grows from even the black-and-white reproduction of color. Out went the gray and sepia—in came blue milk and green lipstick. Today TV advertisers have lost their fear of color in black-and-white, but there are still a few techniques that they must remember.

The starting point for coloring a black-and-white TV presentation is a median color—a medium-value blue-green is such a color, so is the middle value of olive green, and so is a certain tan. Using this basic type of color, you can usually avoid getting colors too close in value yet not in too strong contrast by keeping contrasts on either side of the median color 50 per cent apart.

The safest color is one equivalent to a 30 per cent gray, but you have to choose this color with care. Some colors will give extraordinary contrast; pink and dark brown, for example, televise as black and white. On the other hand you may lose contrast—certain blues and greens in juxtaposition come out as a blob of black.

As a matter of fact it is the blues and greens—the cool colors —that do best in black-and-white TV. They reproduce well and they create an effect of depth which you cannot get with similarly scaled tones of gray.

But now the happy days of green lipstick for black-and-white TV are ending. The villain: compatible color. The TV industry has been nicely straddling the problem of introducing its color to its viewers by transmitting programs in compatible color— a technique that will probably be with us for quite a while. In compatible color some viewers see their spectacular show in color; some in black-and-white. This means that the colors in the production must be suitable to both media. The demand for compatible color doubles the color problems of TV by compounding those of black-and-white and color. Once again, the TV advertiser who takes to the air waves without knowing what his colors are going to do beforehand puts himself in an embarrassing position. He is just as much in the dark as if he had his styling office design his product in a lightless room. It takes a professional knowledge of color and lighting to predetermine what colors will do in the half-and-half world of compatible color.

THE NEED FOR RESEARCH

Color TV is no place for the do-it-yourself develop-your-own-colors enthusiast. TV advertising rates are high, and trial-and-error color selection can run you into a good deal of money with a singular absence of profit.

Color TV is the place for some intensive research. We are going to have to know more about colors, lighting, and texture —we are going to have to manproof the use of colors and color combinations. This calls for a concerted industry-wide research program, and it will take professional color engineering to do the job.

We are going to have to find out and disseminate the following information:

1. Which colors appear and combine to best advantage on color TV.

174

2. Which colors appear and combine to best advantage on black-and-white.

3. Which colors appear and combine to best advantage on both.

4. What positions colors take on a video lightness-and-darkness scale.

5. Which colors and combinations appear best under each type of illuminant.

Without basic information of this nature the TV industry at large and advertisers in particular will continue to flounder on questions of color. With such information they will be briefed for more assured selling success in the most complex color medium man has yet devised.

THE PRICE TAG ON COLOR

While color television naturally costs somewhat more than black-and-white, the difference is not nearly so great as many advertisers have feared. According to an NBC executive, the additional 15–25 per cent that it might cost to have a network program colorcast is actually 5–10 per cent of the advertiser's total time-plus-program outlay. Color at this time generally means extra on-camera rehearsal, more lighting and additional crew members. A film commercial in color might cost only about 15 per cent more than a black-and-white version; color increases the price of animation by 10 per cent or less. Of the thirty stations now accepting live-color commercials, twenty-five charge nothing extra for time and nineteen make no charge for production.

Is color worth the extra cost and trouble? It is already evident that in television—just as in other fields—color pays off in king-size benefits to advertisers. It pays off, that is, providing it is used intelligently and skillfully.

Recently, a test was conducted by a major advertising agency in conjunction with NBC to study the impact of color TV on an average Midwestern town. The results show that:

175

1. Color was found to boost viewing.
2. More viewers per set were noted in color homes.
3. Color was found to increase product recall.
4. Color increases the inclination to buy.

The fact that color helps strengthen impressions is particularly important; as many advertisers know to their chagrin, people forget all too readily. Dr. Walter Scott of Northwestern University established that 25 per cent of a group of people forgot an impression in one day, 50 per cent in two days, and 85 per cent in four days.

In a special report on color, *Television Magazine* points out that many advertisers have already welcomed the chance to grasp the fundamentals of a fabulous new medium while it is still in its initial stages. In this way, they are protecting their investment by experimenting now. And, as color circulation gathers momentum, they will be getting extra impact in color TV homes.

Yes, color TV promises to be an immensely effective advertising medium. You have only to sit in a control room and view a simultaneous showing of a program in black-and-white and color to realize the tremendous increase in visual value and interest color insures. How well sponsors use color in planning commercials and, consequently, in planning their products and packaging, will have a great influence on the agencies' and sponsors' profit picture. Never underestimate the power of the wrong color.

A TALE OF TWO PROGRAMS

Color on television can create a valuable boost or a costly bust—depending on how imaginatively and professionally it is used. This is clearly shown by the following reviews of two actual programs. The material is adapted from my "Color Letter," a monthly feature of *Television Magazine*.

The scene was in old Vienna, and all the "color" backgrounds were used only to convey the atmosphere of "old Vienna." This was done by the obvious method of showing a lot of dark paneling and much bric-a-brac and cluttering background objects. "Old Vienna" came across, but color TV didn't.

In front of this dark, cluttered background the elderly characters wore clothes of neutral colors. This was the color problem—how to convey "old Vienna," elderly people, and drab clothes in scene after scene. The producer's solution was to ignore the problem completely. This wasn't a very wise solution, and anyone who knows anything about color could have solved the problem quickly.

However, the producer was content to ignore the fact that this was supposed to be a "color" presentation. And so a monochrome effect was conveyed, taking away from the mood of the play. In fact, it was sometimes hard to separate the "old characters" from the background of "old Vienna."

The laboratory scene . . . had a dark background with actors in white uniforms. This scene was actually as close to black-and-white as you can get on "color" TV.

Now this black-and-white effect is used very well on the stage during the Ascot scene in *My Fair Lady,* but it was obvious that it was used for no artistic or striking purpose here.

In two other sequences, bowls of bright flowers were practically the only touch of color. Here, someone obviously remembered at the last minute that a "touch of color" was needed. In a banquet scene, a bowl of red roses was placed on the table, in the center foreground. This caught the viewer's attention to the exclusion of the speaker who was behind the red roses. To be consistent, the producer saw to it that this almost invisible speaker was in dark clothes, against a dark background. And so, a major character was "up-staged" by a bowl of flowers. Another first in "color" TV.

The last thing to say about this show is that usually the backgrounds, costumes, hair colors, and complexions were in various shades of completely inconspicuous colors, so that everything had a tendency to take an unwanted color reflection, giving off an iridescent effect that was extremely distracting.

Two of the commercials on this particular program were in color and the others were in black-and-white. The standard background for all announcers on this show appears to be a sky blue backdrop with some diamond shaped objects, diminishing in size, emerging from the left side of the screen. Each of these shapes is in a different color of medium chroma and value.

The announcer stands near the right and wears a gray suit and a light blue shirt. Surprisingly enough, the announcer does advertise a different product each time. And each time, the blue of the background diffuses too much throughout the screen, because it is not the right value of blue.

For one of the color ads, the announcer held some kind of hair spray can, I think. Held against the blue background, it was so lost that the viewer couldn't possibly make out what it was.

At the other extreme, a soap package stood out so brightly against the paler colors of those familiar diamond decorations and the familiar gray suit that it looked as if it were superimposed from another film. But at least it stood out, however badly.

Obviously, the standard set was not intended to have any relation to the products which were shown.

All the other commercials were in black-and-white, and were more effective than the commercials in color.

These comments should not be taken as applying to all presentations of this particular program. It has done excellent color work in the past, and undoubtedly will do so in the future.

After this plaint it is a pleasure to observe that some of the dramatic productions are giving increasing evidence of color consciousness in their presentation. An unpretentious play . . . showed a fine regard for settings and costumes appropriate to the theme and designed to display the actors to their best advantage instead of either overpowering them or else causing them to fade into the background. Most of the scenes took place against simple wood cabinets and paneling or against the slightly varied but neutral grays of a stone fireplace. These stayed in the background where they belonged and the actors' faces stood out warmly and vividly. Costumes showed an interesting variation. Some scenes were played down with the participants dressed in inconspicuous grays and dark blues. But the more dramatic sequences were emphasized by the heroine's brilliant blue blouse or the hero's vermilion shirt. Touches such as these, used quite frequently throughout the performance, were especially effective because of the restrained handling of surrounding color and of the sequences preceding and following them. An excellent pace-changing contrast occurred in the dinner scenes. The first of these was an informal setting in which the ranch hands in colorful shirts sat around a red-checked tablecloth in the foreground and against the same wood-paneled cabinet that did not obtrude in any way. The effect as that of a richly painted canvas. Later a more formal dinner party consisted of actors in dark blue and vermilion. Here the background cabinet was embellished with chinaware in much more subdued shades of the same two colors, a fortunate touch that brought both consistency and a suggestion of luxury to the scene.

Throughout there was apparent a nice feeling of balance between warm and cool colors and for the most effective use of simple ingredients.

THE BIG MUSTS

Despite the technical difficulties I have mentioned in this chapter, advertisers must either use color TV or else abandon to their competitors a highly effective competitive selling medium. So one big *must* is "must use color." And the other big *must* is "must master color." Regardless of cost, color TV is the infant giant of modern merchandising.

COLOR IN DIRECT-MAIL ADVERTISING

American business spends more than a billion dollars a year on direct-mail advertising. This is more than it spends for TV ads, nearly twice what it lays out for magazine advertising, almost three times its expenditure for radio commercials. Only newspapers take a bigger slice of the nation's advertising budget. The already immense direct-mail business is still growing, but it is just over the last few years that the practitioners of direct mail have been learning the true dollars-and-cents value of color.

For many years *The New Yorker* Magazine has been running an intermittent department called "Letters We Never Finished Reading." It is a department well calculated to strike cold terror to the heart of the businessman who gets his business from direct mail. The letter that the prospective customer never finished reading is a dead letter. It is a no-sale ring on the cash register. It is just as much a business loss as a bad magazine ad or an unsuccessful product. Fortunately, color can do an admirable job of making sure that your letter indeed gets itself noticed.

180

DIRECT–MAIL COLOR ON THE JOB

Let's look at the cases:

In 1955 the National Wildlife Federation sent out a 26,000-letter mailing, splitting it between a two-color folder and a six-color folder. The six-color folder pulled 8 per cent greater returns; more important, it brought in a 20 per cent greater cash sale.

Another firm split a 10,000-letter mailing among five color combinations. A pink letterhead in a blue envelope drew nearly half of the total replies; orange paper in a blue envelope pulled second best, green paper in blue envelope drew third, white paper in blue envelope and white paper in white envelope fourth and fifth.

Popular Mechanics Magazine, with a 90,000-piece mailing, found that pink return envelopes did the best job of getting replies, with blue, canary, and green following in that order.

Billboard Magazine switched colors on 36,000 outside envelopes. A yellow-orange envelope drew 22 per cent of the replies, with success shading down through pink, green, and kraft (brown), to a standard white envelope which drew only 12 per cent.

The Kiplinger advertising staff finds that a gray reply card with maroon ink does the best job of getting replies.

Fortune Magazine found colored paper pulling up to 35 per cent better than white on a circulation promotion directed to each of three mailing lists.

Even the conservative *Wall Street Journal* puts direct-mail color to work. The newspaper finds that a blue-cloud effect on its envelopes is the best reply puller, and according to Leslie Davis—special assistant to the newspaper's publisher—typing the addresses of form letters in red instead of black considerably improved those letters' results.

DOES DIRECT–MAIL COLOR PAY?

Color printing costs more, and printing costs are plenty high as it is. The businessman therefore is eminently justified in asking his old hard-headed question: Is it worth it?

What do the men in business say?

Tom McElroy, for many years the promotion director of the *Catholic Digest:* " . . . a second color pays for itself if it is used correctly."

Edward M. Mayer, president of the big mailing firm of James Gray, Inc.: "You'll have to find out your own winning color, but contrasting color seems a cinch to increase your replies."

John T. McKenzie, advertising manager of Standard and Poor's Investment Service: "Change color of ink."

In my own experience, color is indeed worth it, so long as it is color correctly developed and tailored to the selling job that your mailing piece must do. The trouble is that only a small percentage of color selection for direct-mail projects is today done by people who understand color. Too often color is the by-product of casual afterthought. Too many colors grow from random selection and whim. Complicated and comprehensive mailing-list schedules have been worked out, agencies and clients spend thousands of dollars getting and training direct-mail copywriters—yet they neglect color, which can be the factor determining legibility and determining whether their costly mailings are even opened.

No piece of mail you send out can afford to miss any selling asset because it has only a moment of a reader's attention. During this moment, it must get attention and interest. It must not offend prejudices. In all this, color of stamps, envelope, letterhead, and typewriter ribbons lend variety to good letters. They are, of course, subordinate to the selling message.

Have you ever stopped to consider the fact that many prospects reached by direct mail are well along in years, with failing eyesight? Skillful color contrasts will increase legibility on a piece of direct-mail advertising. In all probability, they will elicit better returns. So, whenever possible, consider and use such logical assets in your direct-mail selling. Advertising agencies slant their copy to appeal to various age groups. Why don't they expend equal energy in ascertaining the most effective, response-drawing colors? It's a proven color fact, for example, that colors such as rose appeal to older people.

LIFE MAGAZINE: A CASE IN POINT

Impressed by the lack of color imagination in direct mail, I resolved to do something about it. A telephone call to the business department of *Life* Magazine resulted in an appointment with the promotion executives responsible for the appearance of *Life*'s direct-mail selling material.

I pointed out how the plain white envelope and white paper stock used in *Life*'s mailings failed to achieve the degree of interest necessary to influence me even to *open* one of their costly mailings. Why not, I asked, introduce a more exciting format in the *Life* mailings?

After describing what might be done with striking and intriguingly colored envelopes and letterheads, plus color-co-ordinated return cards and additional enclosures, I learned that *Life* employed a series of nine mailings, to sell a reader on renewing his subscription, or to win a new subscriber.

This arrangement lent itself perfectly to the plan I had in mind. Why not build up a series of color schemes with increasing visual impact, so that each succeeding mailing would have greater and greater eye interest for the recipient? The big color guns would be drawn up for *Life*'s seventh letter—the one that carries the greatest persuasive message. So our organization prepared a series of nine colorful and interest-arousing color schemes and design motifs. No two items in any single mailing were the same color. The typewriter ribbon and signature ink were individualized in strikingly contrasting colors.

183

The response to this color-selling scheme was so gratifying that we were called on to establish the over-all appearance of several successive campaigns. This color sales technique is still used by the world's largest weekly publication.

WHAT COLORS SHOULD YOU USE?

Correct color in direct-mail advertising aims to do four jobs. It should:

1. *Embellish your mailing piece* so that it is eye-catching and therefore more likely to stay out of the category of letters that your prospective customers never finished reading.
2. *Make your sales story easier to put across,* and drive home its message through the added visual emphasis color can impart.
3. *Help illustrate the true appearance of your product.*
4. *Help stimulate a desire for possession.*

The color engineer goes about these jobs by exploiting the color dynamics we've already talked about in this book. For example, he knows that the most appealing colors for a summer mailing are the cool colors like turquoise, green, and blue. Certain pastel colors are the best for business-reply cards. White is by and large the worst color for most mailing pieces, but even this can depend on the class of client you are planning to solicit: if your next mailing is aimed at bankers, the color engineer has found that a crisp white bond letterhead is the sales tool for you.

In developing the right color for your mailing, the color engineer relies heavily on testing and experiment. For selecting a color that will have strong staying power in the mind of your recipients, he will draw on tests like that made some years ago by Dr. George Gallup. Dr. Gallup found that men and women differed in the colors they remembered, that women best remembered dark blue, olive green, purple, yellow, and red in that order, while men retained violet, dark blue, olive green, and yellow.

184

The color engineer will look at the season for which you're planning your mailing. Certain seasons raise certain color associations, and a yellow-and-purple Christmas mailing could well set records for color expense down the drain.

Here are the colors most people associate with the important holidays:

New Year's Day—black and white

Washington's Birthday—red, white, and blue

St. Valentine's Day—red and pale blue

St. Patrick's Day—green

Easter—yellow and purple

Arbor Day—green

Mother's Day—red carnation for living mother, white carnation for mother no longer living

Decoration Day, Flag Day, Independence Day—red, white, and blue

Labor Day—blue

Hallowe'en and Thanksgiving Day—orange and brown

Christmas Day—red and green

You should look closely at the combined visual effect of your paper and ink. Developing a good ink color for white paper stock is never difficult; it's when you want to combine, correctly, colored paper stock with colored ink that you face the psychological and physical characteristics of color. If your paper stock is light in color, ink must be dark to provide contrast and insure visibility. If the paper stock should be grayed, it takes a stronger and more intense ink color to help insure proper legibility. Paper and ink colors that are near each other in value are hard to read—there have been book jacket titles printed in black ink on maroon paper, and in yellow ink on white paper, that were barely legible.

The power of color should be considered. Colors with the strongest visual punch are yellow, orange, and red. But they must be used carefully. Red on a black background lacks the power and eye appeal of the same red against blue-green. And the conventional printing colors are far from being the safe ones. Recently I designed a highly successful promotional booklet which combines chartreuse, orange, purple, black, and emerald green, five colors which have long been relative strangers to the direct-mail business, alone or in combination.

THE TEN KEYS TO DIRECT–MAIL COLOR

There are ten color axioms which best summarize how color can help improve the selling power of your direct-mail campaign.

1. Insure reader interest by giving your mail added visual value through color co-ordination.

2. Accentuate your symbol and trade-mark, and carry through the selling punch of your established company colors.

3. Weigh costs carefully—color is relatively inexpensive compared to the total cost of sending out a mailing.

4. Enhance the selling appeal of your mailing's paper stock through color, but use a paper color which won't negate the appearance of any artwork or design that you plan to run on the paper.

5. Use color for special visual effects.

6. Use unusual and attractive color combinations.

7. Keep a file of color harmonies and color combinations which prove to be effective.

8. Give your printer an actual sample of the colors you want. Don't rely on color names; they are far from standardized.

9. Vary colors in continuous mailings so recipients won't treat your latest mailing as old stuff for the wastebasket.

10. Use four-color work where your product's eye appeal makes the extra expense warranted.

COLOR IN MAKE-UP

Tempting Touch, Clear Clear Red, Twilight Blush, Cheery Cherry, Pink Secret, Cherries in the Snow, Fatal Apple, Cinderella's Pumpkin, Where's the Fire?, Paint the Town Pink, Red Hellion, Carrot Top—the roster of America's cosmetic colors is a startling example of color run wild.

In no other field of American industry today does color have so much to say about sales. The business of cosmetics is the business of color, and manufacturers and sellers have been making the most of color. In 1957, according to the Toilet Goods Association, Americans spent $420,590,000 for cosmetics. Another $387,430,000 went for hair preparations—shampoos, dyes, rinses, home permanents; $84,930,000 bought hand preparations—lotions and nail polishes, largely; $27,130,-000 went for make-up bases. In a vast number of these sales, color was the crucial selling factor.

How about this rainbow of color? Do we need all these cosmetic colors and are we doing a good job of exploiting them? This chapter will attempt to answer these questions.

187

HOW COSMETIC COLORS WORK

Let's look at the second question first. Do manufacturers and sellers make full use of the colors they offer their consumers, or do they dump new colors onto the market without considering how those colors are going to work? Too often, they do the latter. It is a disturbing method, for the rules of color in make-up are just as soundly rooted in the psychology and dynamics of color as are the examples we've seen in previous chapters.

How does color work in make-up? It is a question every manufacturer and seller ought to be able to answer. Here are a few of the ways:

The Mouth: Vivid rouge and lipstick can dramatize it. At the same time these can flash so much color from the mouth that the lips eclipse all other features. Omitting cheek rouge will focus interest on the mouth, and a delicately tinted foundation and powder help to sharpen the color contrast of red lips. Matching nail polish will help emphasize lipstick color.

The Nose: Light-colored powder or no powder at all will accent it if it is a good nose.

The Oval Face: Omitting cheek rouge will accentuate it; so will rouging lips into a more perfect oval themselves.

The Eyes: Shadow, matched in color to the iris and put on heaviest just above the eyelashes, will point them up. Shadow fading outward and upward to the eyebrows from the center of the lid will make eyes look more widely spaced.

These are color effects that every manufacturer must consider in the marketing of his product. These are effects that must be brought to the consumer's attention. If the consumer finds out about these and similar color effects on her own and the result is not to her liking, it may spell the end of a sale in this highly competitive market.

WHAT COLORS?

In promoting their cosmetic lines, manufacturers and dealers should tie in their product colors with three factors: hair color, eye color, and complexion.

Hair and eyes, for example, are the determining factors in helping your customers select the right color for their lipstick. Here is a workable color table relating lipstick colors to hair-eye combinations:

HAIR AND EYE COLOR	CORRECT LIPSTICK COLOR
Blond hair with brown eyes	Pinkish reds and coral reds
Ash blond hair with blue eyes	Pinkish reds and red reds
Auburn hair with brown or green eyes	Peppery reds and red reds
Red hair with blue or gray eyes	Orange reds and coral reds
Medium brown hair with hazel or gray eyes	Blue reds and pink reds
Brown hair with blue or brown eyes	Red reds and bluish reds
Black hair with blue eyes	Red reds and pinkish reds
Black hair with brown eyes	Crimson reds and dark bluish reds
Gray hair with blue or brown eyes	Pink reds and red reds

Hair color is equally important in determining colors for make-up other than lipstick, and—very important—for clothes and accessories. If one of your customers favors yellow-green clothing, for example, she will do well not to dye her hair blond. The redhead is wise in steering clear of red-purple lipstick. Here is a table listing hair colors, and the colors which *don't* flatter them:

BLONDE WOMEN SHOULD AVOID:
   Light intense * reds, grayed reds
   Intense yellow-red of medium value *

   Dark, intense yellows
   Grayed, dark yellow-green, or intense light yellow-green
   Light, grayed greens

* *Value* in this table refers to lightness or darkness; *intensity,* to the purity (as opposed to the grayness) of the color—what colorists call *chroma.*

189

RED-HAIRED WOMEN SHOULD AVOID:
Intense yellow-red
Dark-grayed yellows
Intense red-purples, medium values

LIGHT BRUNETTES SHOULD AVOID:
Grayed yellow-reds, intense yellow-reds
Dark yellows, grayed yellow
Very dark yellow-green, intense yellow-green
Light purple-blue, intense purple-blue
Intense purple, medium values

DARK BRUNETTES SHOULD AVOID:
Medium-intensity and -value yellow-reds
Dark yellows, grayed yellows
Medium-value and dark yellow-green, in weak or strong intensity
Intense blue-green
Light or intense purple-blue
Very intense purple

WHITE-HAIRED WOMEN SHOULD AVOID:
Intense reds
Intense yellow-reds and yellow-reds of medium value
All but grayed, medium value, and dark medium-intensity yellows
Intense greens of light and medium values
Intense blue-greens of light and medium values
Very light and very intense blues
Purple
Intense purple-reds

GRAY-HAIRED WOMEN SHOULD AVOID:
Intense reds
Medium- and strong-intensity yellow-reds in medium values
Light and medium-value intense yellow-greens
Dark, grayed greens
Blue-green
Very light, very intense blues
All very intense shades
Purple
Light purple-red when grayed or very strong intensity; medium-value purple-red of strong intensity; dark, grayed purple-red.

Complexion is still another important factor in determining what make-up colors—and other colors—your customers should buy. Let's see how complexion is affected by color.

THE BRUNETTE: Dark gray makes the brunette look sallow. With bright lavender her complexion appears yellowish. *But she can wear light gray and very vivid colors.*

THE REDHEAD: The redhead tends to look flushed in the usual pinkish shades. Blue-green gives ther complexion a violet cast. *But she looks well in true greens; and rust tones and faded pinks are becoming to her.*

THE BLONDE: Yellow makes the blonde look sallow. A dark bright blue makes her look pale. *But a lighter blue complements the warm tints in her complexion and a deep pink reflects and emphasizes them.*

THE WHITE-HAIRED WOMAN: The white-haired woman looks faded in black and very pale in yellow-green. *But rose pink brings out the delicate shades of her complexion, and so does light blue.*

GLASSES

Glasses and their frames complicate the make-up problem. The color of the frames—and of the lenses if they are tinted—needs to be taken into account in co-ordinating make-up colors with skin and hair tones. The Bausch and Lomb Optical Company had this to say:

An olive-skinned brunette can wear glasses with red frames because the color brightens the skin. Black frames accent fair skin, dark hair and eyes, while brown will flatter the brown-eyed woman who wants to be conservative.

In general, tones of brown, blue, green, or gold look best if your hair is blond and your eyes are blue, green, gray or hazel. If your eyes are brown and your hair is blond, the demi-blond or brown tones are good. Black is fine if your hair has a golden glint.

Brunettes have a wide choice. Red, green or gold look dramatic with dark eyes.

The red-haired woman must be careful. Dark colors are best, especially cinnamon or ebony. Some shades of green are flattering.

191

HOW MANY COLORS?

The color names at the beginning of this chapter are surface manifestations of a problem we have seen again and again in this book—the latter-day profusion, too often a haphazard profusion, of color.

Do we need all these colors? Many manufacturers apparently think so. *Barron's* Magazine reports that "American women are starving for new beauty aids. They will apparently try anything that promises to heighten their physical charms, provided the promise is properly worded and convincingly told by advertising men. The ladies don't expect too much: a new fragrance, a novel shade, a lipstick that stays on a little longer, a powder that spreads more evenly . . . or merely a package that is handier or more attractive will suffice . . . the craving for something 'new' is apparently insatiable."

I believe that the same approach we have discussed in the field of product color and home color applies to cosmetics. I think that there are *too many* colors, and that the cosmetic manufacturer who first realizes and exploits this fact will—despite the apparent color starvation reported by that magazine article—exploit it to his immense profit.

Instead of nine or ten or twenty different shades of red for lipsticks, for example, three or four would do as well. Take three colors: orange red, magenta, and dark red. Used with a light or heavy touch as required, these three shades can closely approximate any of the fabulous spectrum of Cheery Cherry, Where's the Fire? and Red Hellion. It is doubtful that anyone is really going to care whether our three-color lipstick customer's lips are half a shade more lavender or orange; at best they will notice that her lips are slightly lavender or slightly orange or just plain red. Cutting down the numbers of colors is not going to cut down sales. Women will not put on lipstick any less than they did before. And the convenience of a three-lipstick kit supplying a virtually complete color range for a tenth of the cost and inconvenience of maintaining the present lipstick rainbow is going to make more money, I believe, for the manufacturer with the fortitude to launch such a kit.

Face powder is another product where color has gotten out of hand. Nowadays many women are blending loose powder themselves, and if this trend continues the present profusion of powder colors will be unnecessary. Four colors—a dark rosy shade, a lighter rosy shade, a dark tan, and a light tan with a slightly yellowish cast—will readily mix to form any shade of face powder the consumer wants.

New colors can create consumer demand, at least temporarily. The word "new" contains a lot of selling magic. But consumers are becoming more and more color-wise, and the wiser they get, the more selective they get. One of these days cosmetics manufacturers, like so many others, are going to find that it's not the number of colors that sell—it's the correct color magic and the correct color guidance.

COLOR IN WOMEN'S WEAR

The man splashes along in his mate's wake when it comes to using clothes color as a personality asset. Women are far more interested than men in new colors and color-ensemble ideas.

This means that while the seller of men's clothes faces the ghastly job of making the male color-conscious in the first place, the seller, designer, and manufacturer of women's clothes must meet an entirely different problem. Their market is already color-prone. Their problem is not so much convincing women to buy colors as knowing which colors they will buy. This requires a good knowledge of the mechanics of color and how they affect women's clothes buying, a knowledge which should be part of the technical equipment of everybody in this complex business from seamstress to salesgirl.

COLOR AND GOOD TASTE

The same good-taste color rules that operate in the arts, in home decoration, or in any other place where we use color apply to clothing color.

There should be a proper balance between intense and sub-dued shades.

There should be a proper balance between light and dark shades.

There should be a proper balance between warm and cool shades.

It is safest to keep the main parts of a costume in a reasonably subdued shade, and to use a brighter accent color for small areas like hats, bags, gloves, collars, and blouses. The brighter the color of these areas, the fewer or smaller they should be.

The reverse of this effect is also a good color use. Black accessories will set off a very bright dress.

Bright shades and bold color contrast emphasize the wearer's good points. If she has lovely eyes but big feet, she should wear simple shoes in black, dark brown, or navy and draw attention to her eyes with a bright and frivolous hat. If her feet are slim and graceful, however, bright red, white, or pastel shoes or even multicolored ones will highlight them.

Correct color can appear to modify a woman's stature. If she's tall she can wear a vivid dress but not with too bright a hat—the hat would call attention to her height. If she's short, a hat matching her coat or dress in bright colors will make her look taller. If she's heavy, dark colors in simple lines will make her look slimmer. If she's thin, she'll shape up in light colors.

Certain mistakes in the use of color show up all the time. The worst of these, though not the most obvious, is the wearing of several shades of a color that do not quite match. It does not matter so much if a shade is somewhat lighter or darker than another with which it is worn, but if it is slightly different in hue but not different enough to afford an intentional contrast the effect will be haphazard and careless. It is also a mistake for a woman to wear too many colors, or several different figured materials.

HOW MUCH COLOR SHOULD WOMEN WEAR?

The amount of color depends on some of the general color rules we've already touched on. A vivid woman with strongly contrasting hair and skin color can wear an entire costume of emerald green or vermilion. The same colors would engulf the mousy girl. The mouse, however, *can* use these colors as accents to call attention to her best features. The woman who can wear a whole costume of vivid color needs only a few touches of neutral shades. The girl who relies on bright hues for accent only will of course wear a conservatively colored basic costume.

WHICH COLORS?

The man in the women's clothes business is faced with a multiple problem: what amount of color to turn loose on the market, in what combination, and which colors. The last is a nagging problem indeed. The answer depends a great deal on the associations we've developed with color, and on the coloring of the people who are going to buy our clothes. Let's look first at some examples of color associations and what effect they have on women's clothing:

1. *Black is a protective hue.* It is excellent as a suit color for the girl who is job hunting. If yellow or gold is added as an accent, say in a blouse, she is still more likely to get the job, for yellow is the color to wear when one wishes to shine in conversation and to establish self-confidence. A woman will always accept a black dress as a color but will never choose a color to substitute for black.

2. *Blue is subtle* and more directly influential than red. It inspires interest in the male. Blue is not an exciting color to wear but as with an old friend, it does not readily tire us.

3. *A green dress can have sex appeal* since certain greens symbolize sociability, tenderness, and intensity.

196

4. *A bluish-violet dress appeals to spiritual types.* It seems to help make people more emotionally interested in the wearer.

5. *White represents calmness, composure, and savoir-faire.* It enhances other colors as an accent.

6. *Silver imparts charm and glamour.*

7. *Gold,* worn as an accent in a bracelet, clasp, or earrings, *has a luminous effect* on the person of the wearer.

REGIONAL PREFERENCES

Regional preferences also have a strong influence on the color decisions the women's-wear maker and dealer must face. Let's look at some.

In the South women prefer blues.

The ruddy complexions of New England influence clothes buying favorable to those complexions. Incidentally, New England and the Midwest harbor many blondes—partly because of a concentration of people of Swedish descent—and these blondes have special color preferences too.

In Texas there is always a strong surge toward beige in post-Christmas buying.

COLOR TRENDS

Another factor that influences women's-wear color decisions is color trends. There are fashions in colors as well as in styles, and it's important to keep your eye on the people who set those trends.

The piece-goods people, for example, usually determine the color trends in women's wear. They are always looking out for new colors which they think will sell—often they exploit a new color by joining forces with a couturier like Balenciaga and deciding what new colors will be promoted and how. When they decide on their promotion colors they will put them on the market with a forced-draft sales campaign; each new color available in all fabric lines and all price ranges.

197

Department stores also set color fashions. Take Neiman-Marcus in Dallas. They will go to considerable expense to promote a color *per se*—some time ago, when Stanley Marcus was merchandising yellow, he called their color "Canary Yellow" and filled their window displays with eye-catching canaries, in the feather.

I saw the effect of Neiman's high-pressure high-temperature color merchandising when I supervised a color survey in Dallas. Many of the women stated frankly that they had not made up their minds on clothing color but were standing by waiting for Neiman-Marcus's next promotion. As far as they were concerned, they liked anything Neiman-Marcus chose to sell.

Other trend setters in the woman's clothing business include individuals and unsatisfied customers.

For example, Countess Mona Bismarck (formerly Mrs. Harrison Williams), a perennial inhabitant of the best-dressed lists, favors purple; her taste has often swung public preference to a previously unwanted shade.

Dissatisfied customers start color trends through the agency of smart manufacturers. Many manufacturers collect all the color requests they can't fill from their current stock, then look them over and evaluate them. Time and time again these unfilled requests prove to be the most wanted colors for the next season.

Some firms go to extraordinary lengths to anticipate and satisfy color trends. Forstmann Woolens, for example, has an exceptionally flexible line, set up so that the company can dye-match any important new color just as soon as that color appears to be catching the wave of public acceptance.

The ultimate decision in the business, of course, is up to the consumer. That means that the manufacturer, distributor, and seller have to anticipate color trends and try to meet them. If a man is in the shoe business with its lengthy dyeing process this requires some perspicacious anticipation. The conclusion: the more color facts you have on hand, the better your decisions are going to be.

CLOTHING AND COMPLEXION

Of strong importance to the manufacturer and retailer is the effect of complexion on clothing—and of clothing on complexion. Women consider their complexions carefully before they buy clothes. The only trouble is they frequently don't know enough about color to come up with a proper choice. If *you're* briefed on the interrelationship of color and complexion, you can brief your customers in turn. You can turn them out in correct colors correctly chosen, and that'll keep 'em coming back for more.

Female companion types subdivide into eight groups:

Pale Blonde	Dark Brunette
Medium Blonde	White Hair
Ruddy Blonde	(Peroxided hair,
Redhead (Titian)	or Albino types)
Light Brunette	Gray Hair

The *pale blonde* has light blue eyes, light yellow hair, and fair skin. The *medium blonde* has hair of a lower value than pale or ruddy blondes; eyes gray, green, or pale blue; skin of a neutral tone. The *pale* or *medium blondes* are fortunate. Their natural coloring imposes few restrictions on their choice of colors. In general, they may wear any hues except certain yellows —yellow furnishes no contrast for their hair, and tends to throw a slight greenish hue into their white skin. Pastels of brown, blue, and green are ideal, while dark colors are equally effective because they serve as a foil for the fair hair and skin. Grays, however are generally unbecoming to *all* pale blondes—especially in the evening. Black is particularly becoming to blondes who have strong natural coloring; it enhances the rose of their complexion. But it should be avoided by the very pale, because of its tendency to bleach natural color by contrast. A rosy color can be imparted to a pale complexion with a bright blue-green scarf near the face.

The difference in the other suitable hues for the costume of the pale and medium blonde is small. Both can wear all reds except those of weak chroma. Both can wear yellow-reds of a very light or very dark value. The pale blonde should choose those of weak to vivid chroma. Both should avoid intermediate hues—yellowed reds of both weak and strong chroma, the hues between orange and red and orange and yellow in the spectrum. In green-yellow, the pale blonde should select dark values from weak to vivid chroma variations; the medium blonde, dusky values of vivid to strong chroma. The medium blonde can wear all variations of blue-green; blue; purple-blue; purple or red-purple. The pale blonde should avoid very weak chroma strength of these colors.

The *ruddy blonde* has a high pink-and-white coloring; blue eyes, and hair tending to the yellow. She is somewhat more restricted in her choice, since reds and yellows and all colors in which these hues appear tend to increase the ruddiness of any overflushed or too rosy complexion. However, she may safely select high-value reds of very weak purity (pinks) or dark-value reds of vivid or strong chroma (maroons). Any person with bright natural coloring is an ambulatory example of the law of simultaneous contrast: adjacent areas of strong color, whether complementary or contrasting, tend to heighten each other's purity.

The *light brunette* has medium light hair, some natural color, brown, blue or hazel eyes, and fair, or perhaps neutral skin tone. She can wear any color she chooses, with the single exception of the yellowish browns. She looks well in high-value pastel colors.

The *dark brunette,* with olive skin, vivid coloring, dark eyes, and dark brown or black hair, can wear any strong-chroma color regardless of hue.

The *red-haired* type, with a fair skin, blue or brown eyes, and hair shades anywhere from "carrot" to auburn, should avoid red by itself and colors in which red appears. These will detract from the brilliance of her hair. A pink dress, unless it is a grayish or bluish hue of pink, imparts a yellowish look to her hair. For this type, rich gay gleaming emerald green, reddish brown, blue-gray or lapis blue are among the very best-looking colors. They can be worn in as bright a chroma strength as desired.

It is just as important for the redhead type to suit her skin color as her hair, in choosing her costume. If she has flawless skin, black is a striking color for her. If her skin is freckled or spotted, the redhead had better stick to cool colors—blues and greens. In this connection it is interesting to observe that only one person in every forty thousand of the population has naturally red hair and only one in seventy thousand is favored with titian-hued tresses.

The *white-haired* type has a unique problem in choosing costume colors. Her skin and eye pigmentation is usually that of the pale blonde. In the main, she may follow the rules for that type. Her hair being lighter in value than yellow, she may wear, moreover, some of the high-value, weak-chroma variations of this hue. If she is a true Albino and pink-eyed, she must avoid nearly all hues on the warm side of the spectrum, except red-purple and pink. Greens in weak chromas but all values will be charming on her. So will be either black or white. Gray is generally recognized as the color of age, representing both maturity and sophistication. It tends to draw from neighboring colors. However grays are notably unbecoming to white-haired people although it seems that when in doubt as to what color to wear they invariably wear gray.

The woman with gray hair does not always mean the older woman. The peculiar composition of some hair is such that it early loses pigmentation and becomes a neutral tone which may range anywhere from silver to a deep iron gray. The woman with hair prematurely gray need not lament her state, for there are numerous ways in which a well-groomed gray head can be set off handsomely with a proper choice of color in the costume. Gray, being a neutral, is friendly with all hues. Almost all variations of color are possible in the dress of the gray-haired type, although if she has lusterless, mousy hair, she will be most successful if she sticks to the shades and tints outlined for the medium blonde. If her hair is gray due to age, her skin too is apt to have yellowed somewhat or lost its freshness. The older woman may counteract this by wearing cool, clear colors of not too harsh a chroma, and by avoiding pastels, muddied shades, and of course all yellows.

SOME MORE COLOR RULES

There are two special color rules to consider:

Black is kind to the woman's size but tough on her outline. White, on the other hand, makes her look bigger but not in specific places. This means that if she has a good figure black is the better of the two colors, especially if she is large. There is one more condition to wearing black—it highlights the defects in a bad complexion, and the woman afflicted with such a complexion will therefore do well to avoid it.

Exploit color co-ordination. It's a big seller and a handy sales tool. In England they're selling candy boxes in colors especially designed to blend or contrast with milady's gown. A New York shop recently marketed a Dodge Motor Coat made out of car upholstery fabric—"a coat to match your car interior." All the color mechanics we've talked about in this section stand up effectively when exploited for color co-ordination.

COLOR CREATES DEMAND

One excellent case history of the diverse color influences which impinge on the American market appears in the women's shoe business. Here's what Dorothea B. Warren, one of the top shoe stylists, has to say about that proliferation of influences.

Predicting fashion colors for shoe retailers is an intricate and involved decision. . . . There are so many factors that must be considered, especially since we work so far in advance of the ready-to-wear market. Shoe colors are studied at least six months in advance of the time a consumer ever sees them. . . . There are many types of color to consider . . . high fashion colors . . . basics, the neutrals, the classics, the shock, the pastels and often off-beat shades.

Many times a color may not be eye-catching and may even be considered drab, but the use of a color by a fashion colorist will be the reason for its success. . . . An important play may be an influence, for example, "My Fair Lady," which has had a great impact on the fashion market. There are often emotional reactions to color . . . for example, the clear Vinylite plastic shoe . . . so prevalent in our market today, is a good example of an emotional reaction by the customer. The reason this has become so wanted is that a woman experiences a great lift—it is flattering, it is unusual . . . the magic of Cinderella still exists.

It's a full-time job keeping tabs on color influence ranging from *My Fair Lady* to Cinderella, and foreign manufacturers are so remote from these factors and so unfamiliar with them that even if they tried to do the full-time job, they wouldn't be able to do it with profitable proficiency and success. In foreign countries, demand creates the supply, but in this country, it is the new, well-launched color theme that creates the demand.

COLOR IN MEN'S WEAR

Three centuries ago, Europe's gentlemen were walking about in green doublet and breeches, set off with a lace collar and bright taffeta sash around the waist. From there on up to the present, color in men's wear has been a sometime thing—at one period outshining women's finery, at another retreating to dress men in the workaday coloration of a pall bearer.

Men's clothes and their colors have been, at one time or another, a mark of a man's station, an indication of his trade, and a problem for legislative and judicial concern. When Elder Bradford wrote describing the Pilgrims he noted that "There's not a wealthy man among them—not a patch of purple." By 1634 wealthy men were appearing in the colonies and the General Court of Massachusetts felt impelled to note that too much money and material was being spent on "some newe and immodest fashions"; it told the colonists that "Noe person, either man or woman, shall hereafter make or buy apparrell, either woollen, silk or lynnen, with any lace on it, silver, golde, silke, or thread."

Color cycles in the eighteenth and nineteenth centuries

dressed the dandy of the French Empire in a blue tail coat, wide canary-yellow nankeen trousers, a top hat, and pumps, but by 1839 a gentleman's visiting costume had subsided to a reddish-brown waisted coat and long gray trousers. By the 1880's colors were back on the upgrade, perhaps reaching their bright point on a morning in the summer of 1887 when Berry Wall, a young man with an independent income, appeared in the lobby of Saratoga's Grand Union Hotel wearing a red doeskin suit.

With the twentieth century clothes colors for men staged a long-term retreat. Lord Curzon could look down his nose at brown and millions of men would listen. Clothes became multi-purpose in their drabness—one suit could serve for sport or dress. By 1954 a college graduate, writing in his Alumni Bulletin, could report that a student had negotiated his way through the entire social curriculum of four years of college with one suit and four pairs of war-surplus khaki pants.

At mid-century the lackluster look in man's clothing appears to be nearing its welcome end. The first break in the bleakness barrier came after World War II with an explosive increase in demand for colored sportswear.

COLOR IN SPORTSWEAR

The tremendous vogue for colorful sportswear has brought a proliferation of bright shirts, slacks, and jackets; playfully patterned Yeddo straws; Tyrolean hats in greens, rusts, and heather shades; caps in the gayest of pinwheel colors. Obviously men like the colors, and the folks who say they don't are fast adjusting their sights. Man's desire for clothing has been pent up for three generations; sportswear allows him, for the first time in too long a time, to express his personal color taste in what he wears.

There is no limit to the uses of color in sports outfits. There is no limit to its abuses, either, and the manufacturer who fails to recognize this is letting himself in for a sharp dip in the sales curve. Take the problem of compatibility. Single garments (one trusts) are rarely worn on their own; we wear them in combination with other garments and accessories, with shoes and caps and belts and hats. Mix and match has been the watchword for many clothes manufacturers—the trouble is that too often their products don't mix and don't match.

A few years ago I came face to face with this problem in a job I did for McGregor Sportswear, the largest manufacturer of men's sport clothes in the world. I was asked to evolve colors for McGregor shirts, jackets, and slacks which would be compatible with each other; the company wanted the items in its line interchangeable. Moreover the colors had to appeal not to men alone but also to the women who buy at least one-third of men's sportswear. I cut McGregor's line two-thirds to a set of twelve profitable colors—among them mahogany, lime, and toast—which are capable of a huge number of compatible combinations. David Doniger, president of the firm, has summarized the results: "The colors are all interchangeable—a man can mix them up any way he wants without danger of clashing."

One of the focal points for the impact of the new blooming of color in sportswear has been the clothing store; nobody recognizes the importance of the new color trends better than the retailer. Robert B. Underwood, president of Richmond's Berry-Burk and Company, summarized this nicely in a recent letter: "Sportswear is becoming a way of life, even with the most conservative gentlemen, and most men's wardrobes include a liberal supply of sport coats, sport shirts, sweaters, and tee shirts—in keeping with the new trend to casual living."

COLOR IN BUSINESS WEAR

Color in business wear is still meeting some durable sales resistance—the gray flannel suit remains the uniform of the day for much of America's male working population.

But even in this field color is picking up tremendous momentum as a sales tool. There are several influences responsible for color's invasion into this traditional province of male drabness. One is the latter-day appearance of colorful business clothes in Europe. Italian men, for example, wear patterned suits in the winter, bright blue and green lightweight suits in the summer. Haberdashery in other countries has been showing a similar bloom of color, and much of this cheerful merchandise is finding its way into the American market where it is giving domestic clothing a strong run for the money.

A second influence now injecting color into the business clothing world is the work of a few sartorial evangelists. Several men are currently trying to persuade the American male to come out of his colorless cocoon. An outstanding member of this clan of color crusaders is Raymond Godfrey Twyeffort, past president of the National Association of Merchant Tailors of America and sponsor in this country of the colored dinner jacket and tartan tuxedo. Ray Twyeffort is articulate and eminently quotable on the lack of color in business clothing. "Civilization has given us gray flannel suits," he says. "Adam didn't wear gray flannel. He wore a fig leaf and that's green. I don't even own a gray flannel suit. I'm no mouse."

At other times Twyeffort has pointed out that "Color is male. Look back at the Indians; cowboys who dyed their shirts bright red; lumberjacks in colors as varied as the leaves of a tree; the Northwest Mounted Police. They were men."

Twyeffort's conclusion from this evidence is a call for sartorial revolt. "Office girls know how to dress to attract the boss. Why not you? Let's quit looking like penguins, men, and bring on the peacocks."

The peacock look may be a few years in the offing, but color is still beating at the fortress of bleak business dress. A recent *New York Times* article noted that "the blue serge psychology is dead . . . this development has seen men's suits move through the gray-flannel craze, the charcoal gray era and the Ivy-League style. Now some are going from dark to lighter shades."

Berry-Burk's Bob Underwood has expanded on this theme, too: "Color is becoming increasingly important each season . . . dark olive green and gray greens, wine and black, and brown and black combinations are important in suits and sport coats, particularly for the Ivy League adherents; so are accessories with deep tone neckwear—especially in Repp silks and English wools and Challis. Clothing is becoming more alive, and medium shades in suits will supplant the darker tones of past seasons."

COLOR FOR EVENING WEAR

Color has gained a firm foothold in the field of evening wear. The solid-color and plaid dinner jackets, bright cummerbunds, and pastel summer evening clothes are all now well established in the men's furnishing business.

This increase in color has even left its mark on the activities of such bastions of conservative cut and color as New York's famous Brooks Brothers. Influenced to a large extent by the growing acceptance of color, Brooks has introduced an entirely new concept in men's clothing. Until recently men's clothing fell into four categories: business clothing, sportswear, summer-type clothing, and formal clothing. Now Brooks has evolved a fifth category—casual dress for evening. Until this new idea, a man had nothing to change into after he arrived home from business. He had to rely on sportswear, which is more appropriate to the outdoors, or change into a business suit like the one he'd been wearing all day long. Brooks' new line introduced odd jackets and contrasting or co-ordinated slacks in which color played a dominant role. The jackets are in solid shades of unusually attractive red, green, yellow, and black Lanella flannel—the trousers come in no less than thirteen different patterns and colors, including black with tartan stripes down the sides, alternating narrow stripes, all tartan, and checks.

WHAT COLORS DO MEN WANT?

An advertising authority has contrasted the techniques of selling to men and women: to a woman customer, the salesgirl says, "Yes, ma'am, it's exclusive. There's not another like it in town." To a man, the salesman says, "Yes, sir, it's our best seller. You'll see everyone wearing it."

The desire for uniformity in clothing color is apparently well ingrained in the average man—especially when he decides to dress up. Take the new olive drab suits, for example. For years olive green was a hesitant seller in men's clothes; in 1956 it suddenly caught on. The more men who saw other men in the color, the more the color took hold. In the spring of 1956 the Radcliffe Club of New York gave a party for its younger women, inviting a horde of young bachelors. "It was olive green here and olive green there," said one of the ex-Cliff-dwellers later. "It looked like an army camp. Two years ago I tried to get my brother to buy an olive green gabardine jacket. He laughed me out of the house."

How can business deal with the man's apparent desire for protective coloration? What can we do about the masculine prediction for camouflaging himself in the crowd?

Our best bet, undoubtedly, is to capitalize on this desire. If man wants to identify himself with other men, let's help him out. Men's color identifications are many. There are schools, clubs, fraternal orders, sports organizations, military units— all of these have their distinctive colors. These colors can easily go into sweaters, neckwear, mufflers, socks, and other accessories. One of these days a progressive manufacturer of men's wear is going to set up a line of color combinations embracing the most commonly used school and fraternal organization colors, and instruct his retailers to adopt promotional names tying in the colors at point of sale to local schools and fraternal groups. His success should be awesome.

Our second-best bet is to rely on the educational efforts of that more color-conscious member of the buying public, the woman.

Woman's educational efforts may meet stiff resistance, but she is joining battle in a more direct manner by appearing, cash in hand, at the point of sale. Estimates of the percentage of men who buy their clothes under the presumably more color-conscious eye of a distaff consultant run from 30 to 70 per cent. The figure for accessory purchases may be as high as 85 per cent —some retailers think so. The manager of one New York chain states: "About 35 per cent of the men who come in here bring their wives. On Saturday nearly all of them bring women." The executive director of the National Association of Retail Clothiers and Furnishers has recommended that the Association's members make their stores more pleasing to women. Another New York store manager puts it this way: "Before the war, 25 per cent of the men brought women in here with them when they bought clothes. Today women do 70 per cent of the selecting. And sometimes they don't even have the man with them."

Women who shop for men's apparel are torn between their own freedom of approach to color and an awareness of the inhibitions that shackle the male. Place some facts on man's persistent desire to identify himself with a group and its colors in the hands of a woman shopper. Then manufacture those colors. You'll have less difficulty enriching the colors of man's attire along more salable patterns. With this greater freedom of color, men will perforce require larger wardrobes; certainly they won't be able to wear their brighter colors with the day-in, day-out regularity of today's solemn and regulation blues, grays, and browns.

HOW COLOR CAN HELP SALES

There are two other ways in which color can help sales of men's wear. One is color co-ordination. The other is an increased understanding by manufacturers, retailers, and their personnel of the workings of clothing color.

First, color co-ordination. Its importance is growing; it is more and more becoming an essential factor in the successful and profitable operation of the men's wear store or department. Color co-ordination involves stressing the right ensemble—

making sure that customers realize and understand that correct clothing must involve co-ordinated colors. Women have long bought clothes in ensembles—men would do well to emulate this technique and accordingly get the most for their clothing dollar. This means that the manufacturer must make sure that all his clothing line—socks, ties, shirts—is compatible, and that customers are told about this compatibility. In our recent color planning for Holeproof Hosiery, we've kept this consideration strongly in mind. Retailers and manufacturers who are successfully concentrating on this ensembling are finding that they have turned up a fertile field of mass promotion and new and heavier sales.

But ensembling is impossible without an understanding of the visual workings of clothing color. Second, then, let's look at some of the color's effects.

Color Affects Size

Large men look less bulky in dark, conservative, plain colors; small men look larger in strong colors and pronounced patterns. A tall, slender man should not be fitted out in a vertical-stripe suit, but the short, stocky customer will be pleased to find himself lengthening out in a suit with fine, contrasting, pinpoint vertical lines.

Color Affects Complexion

Navy blue—the color of the standard blue suit—goes well with the appearance of most men. But it takes a man with a warm, dark-to-deep complexion to look well in vivid blues.

Purple, a necktie color, does violence to the complexion of the red-haired man.

Browns and *beiges*—frequent shirt and jacket colors—are fine for the red- or coppery-haired man. On the fair-skinned older man they convert him to an undistinguished blur. Gray and blue are his colors.

Yellowish browns, also standard colors, play hob with the appearance of the older man. They tend to produce an unflat-

211

tering yellow tinge on white hair or bald heads.

Pale green, an increasingly popular color in shirting, is a good choice for the olive-skinned Latin type. *The blue shirt* is compatible with most men's suiting and it is flattering to the majority of complexions. *The standard white shirt,* on the other hand, gives most men a clinical appearance—a *creamy white* avoids this and is, moreover, a better match with browns and tans.

These are only a sampling of the color facts that the manufacturer and retailer must learn if they are going to move their merchandise and move it profitably. And learning them they are indeed. Let's hear from Mr. Underwood once more: "Color in apparel is a great boon to merchandisers—and to display and advertising men. . . . We believe in color in good taste. We think the public likes it. It makes us feel more alive. Just look at the automobile!"

COLOR SELLS TODAY'S HOMES

Co-ordinated color is one of the most effective sales tools ever offered to the housing industry. It can be a major aid to manufacturers in selling more products into the house. And it can be a great help to the merchant-builders and planners of developments in selling more houses. But the use of color can be as dangerous as it is exciting, for there are more ways to use color badly than there are ways to use color well.

Nowadays it is easier than ever to use color properly, for so many better colors are available and so much more is known about the principles of good color use, and about how to evaluate consumer color wants well in advance of changes in the cycle of color fashion. A builder has only himself to blame if he fails to get good advice and so fails to cash in on the extra selling potentiality good color can give him.

The best advice to home builders is this: *Get professional color guidance from the qualified color engineer or else stick very closely to the stock color combinations recommended by the manufacturers.* Otherwise you may find buyers backing away from color, mortgage lenders discouraging its use, and appraisers discounting it in their valuations.

Rightly used, color is just about the best way to add value to a house and improve its marketability. Agencies such as FHA, VA, and other appraisers are beginning to reflect that greater visual value in their appraisals.

Again and again it has been revealed how little builders understand about color, and how little color manufacturers understand about home building. The builders do not know about the postwar revolution in color and paint. The manufacturers do not know about the postwar revolution in home building and home finance.

Color manufacturers are proud of the infinite variety of colors and color combinations they can produce. But builders are baffled and frustrated by the very variety of colors in which the manufacturers take such pride. Again and again they make it clear that they want fewer rather than more colors, and they show more concern with the danger that colors used incorrectly might hurt their business than enthusiasm over the chance that colors used smartly might help their business.

The one constant plea of the builders' spokesmen is for help in making the profitable use of color simpler and easier. They have asked the manufacturers and color professionals to get together on colors that are compatible and easy to combine.

WHY ARE HOME BUILDERS SO CONCERNED ABOUT COLORS?

Before the mass-market revolution in home building, few builders had to worry about safety in color selection, for in those days most houses were built to order, to satisfy the taste—or lack of taste—of a known buyer. But today most people buy their homes ready-made, just as they buy their clothes ready-made or their cars ready-made. Today only one house in six is built for a known buyer, and even that one house in six will probably be resold to an unknown buyer within five years.

This is another way of saying that five times out of six the colors, both inside and out, are established before anyone knows what kind of family will buy the house and live in it. So, few builders and lenders feel that they can afford to gamble on colors and color combinations which will not have the broadest common denominator of consumer appeal.

Before the revolution in home building the mortgage lender played a minor part in color selection. Today he is deeply concerned. The builder can take his profit and run once he has found a buyer who likes the colors he has chosen, but the mortgage lender must live with the house for twenty or thirty years through many changes of ownership. He has the biggest stake in the use of safe colors, for he has the most to lose by a color choice that might lower the resale marketability of the house.

For instance, right now the future of the color kitchen is in the lenders' hands. The built-in kitchen that is selling so many houses can be volume-sold only because of two changes in the mortgage pattern: (1) more and more lenders are now willing to cover the appliances with the "package mortgage"; (2) the Housing Act of 1954 made it possible to add a $1,000 built-in kitchen as part of a $15,000 house for only $250 down and thirty years to pay the balance at 4.5 per cent interest.

No builder can use colors his mortgage lender will not finance. So builder and appliance makers alike have the same good reason for adopting safe colors for the built-in kitchen.

KEEP THE NUMBER
OF COLORS UNDER CONTROL

No practical colorist wants to standardize colors or limit the consumer's freedom of choice. But all recognize that the economies of factory-applied color, quantity production, warehousing, and volume building for unknown buyers are working inexorably to make concentration on relatively few colors inevitable.

The more colors used, the more color costs. Cleaning the machinery to shift from color to color is a major factor in paint cost. Cleaning brushes to shift from color to color runs up the labor cost of painting. Warehousing appliances in even half a dozen colors is so costly that most dealers have dragged their feet on color.

Few progressive builders feel they must offer home buyers a choice of more than nine exterior colors, including white. As of 1958, few progressive bathroom-fixture or kitchen-appliance makers offered more than six colors, excluding white. For the kitchen, Frigidaire offered four, General Electric and Westinghouse five. All of them make yellow, green, and pink in addition to white. Amana is featuring a choice of yellow or blue interiors in their 1959 line. After thirty years of color bathrooms, four colors have taken most of the market—pink, blue, green, and yellow. (Standard Sanitary in 1958 offers a choice of eight, Crane six, Briggs six.) Over the years the colors offered by competing manufacturers tend to draw closer, for any very successful color is promptly copied. Yellow promises to be the important feature color to be promoted in house furnishings for 1959.

"SAFE" COLORS AND "STYLE" COLORS

The problem of color in today's house breaks down into two related but very different problems:

1. The problem of colors which are applied at the site and are relatively easy to change. The easiest color source to change is paint and the next easiest is wallpaper.

2. The problem of colors which are applied in the factory and are hard or impossible to change. Colors difficult to change are the baked-enamel finishes on kitchen appliances and steel cabinets. Colors impossible to change include those of ceramic tile, porcelain enamel, and resilient floor covering.

The easier a color is to change, the less important it is to use colors and color combinations no one will actively dislike. But the builder who is not versed in the use and desirability of com-

216

patible colors will insist that his factory-applied colors be muted and neutralized. The strong colors needed for accents and the special colors needed to give each woman a chance to express her individuality he will use only in paint, wallpaper, draperies, towels, bath mats, etc.

TODAY'S KITCHENS
MAGNIFY THE COLOR PROBLEM

Color in the kitchen is a special problem because: (1) the kitchen is being opened up to the living area, so its colors must blend with the living-area color scheme; (2) most kitchen colors are factory applied and are therefore hard to change; (3) competition is improving appliances so fast that home buyers may wish to install a new model long before the old model wears out. How will the new unit's colors fit into the original color scheme —especially if it is a different make?

Sometimes, of course, the builder's color problem in the kitchen and bath is easier than his color problem in other rooms, for each major fixture and appliance manufacturer stands ready not only to suggest the colors which go best with his line, but also to recommend a series of specific products—floor coverings, counter tops, tiles, cabinets—whose factory-applied colors have been co-ordinated with his own.

This means the builder can proceed with color confidence as long as he buys all the major units for the room from a single manufacturer, as he usually does for the bathroom. He is safe unless he tries to split his purchases between two competitive makes, as he often does for the kitchen.

This lack of co-ordination reflects a possible conflict of interest between the manufacturer, who believes he can score a competitive advantage through special colors, and the builder, whose only interest is to get a color-co-ordinated kitchen built in at a cost low enough to help sell the house. The manufacturer tells his dealers: "Once you sell the range in our color, you are sure to get the refrigerator order, too, for no other maker's colors will look right with ours." The builder wants to avoid

217

any such trap and to keep his freedom to pick and choose each appliance in his search for the best product or the best price.

This confusion is being complicated still further by the steel-cabinet makers. Some of them bring out their own gay and often incompatible colors to compete with the new popularity of wood finishes. Others fear they may have to multiply their colors (and their warehousing) to offer cabinets to go with half a dozen semi-incompatible appliance lines.

The color engineers, architects, and builders believe the manufacturers may hurt their own best interests if they push incompatibility too far and make it needlessly hard to use competitive products in the same kitchen. While it is not recommended that the appliance makers standardize or limit their colors, it might be suggested that through their trade associations they should follow either of two lines of action:

1. Get together with the Research Institute of the National Association of Home Builders and make sure their competitive colors will not be so incompatible that they cannot be used in the same room, or so incompatible that the makers of other factory-colored kitchen components will have to multiply their color lines.

2. All offer one or two identical colors along with as many special colors as they want.

Whatever manufacturers do, the builders can protect themselves by using a neutral gray or beige for all their cabinets, letting the appliances stand out as accents against this muted background. They can further reduce the incompatibility problem by using different colors when they use different makes (for example, Frigidaire blue when they use General Electric green, Westinghouse pink, or Kelvinator yellow).

COLOR AND PREFABRICATED HOUSES

An increasing slice of today's home-buying investment is going for the prefabricated house. James M. Lange, executive editor of the authoritative magazine *Practical Builder,* recently estimated that by the 1960's Americans will be demanding more than 1,500,000 new dwellings a year; it is a not unreasonable prediction that fully a quarter of those houses will be prefabricated.

The skillful use of color on prefabricated houses improves eye appeal and makes the house much easier to sell, as well as increases the house's value. I created the exterior and interior colors for the United States Steel Corporation homes with a view to making them a pleasure to look at and a joy to live with. The special range of colors used makes these houses blend with their surroundings—the garden, shrubs, the homes next door, the school or church on the corner. The colors also help express the personality of the family, make the houses distinctive and individual, yet integrate each into the entire community. All of these examples of personalized color designed for use on these homes can be applied in any relationship on the exterior without discord. They provide a modern environment for the family and serve to enhance the spirit of the home and the character of the locality.

But color does much more for houses of this nature. A dark-colored roof, for example, can make a light-colored house appear lower than it really is, while a light roof adds apparent height. Light color on the body areas of a small house will tend to make the house look larger, and dark tones tend to decrease the appearance of size and complement the architectural design features. By introducing contrasting color to emphasize its horizontal lines a house that is too high and narrow can be made to appear wider and lower.

All in all, color does an important selling job for homes like this—it makes them sell faster, and they stay sold.

TODAY'S PAINTS ARE BETTER THAN EVER

Color comes into the home in many ways: paint, roofing, siding, wallpaper. Color is showing up on the host of new building materials that may be revolutionizing the construction business. We're going to look at some of these materials and see what effect they have on color—and what effect color has on them. First, though, let's look at our old friend and stand-by—paint.

Architects, builders, prefabricators, manufacturers, and the color engineers agree that today's paints are very much better than before World War II. The paint manufacturers go further. They say paints have improved more in the last ten years than in all previous history.

Paint progress is so rapid it is almost impossible to set paint standards today which will not be obsolete tomorrow. Even the government's paint-buying standards, although excellent, are hard pressed to keep pace.

For the past twenty years many home buyers have been trying to reduce their exterior painted areas in the hope of cutting future maintenance. More and more consumers are showing a preference for brick because of their belief that brick means lower upkeep. I believe this effort to use less paint would be reversed if more home owners and builders fully understood how much better today's paints are.

Almost everything about today's paints is different except their names. Outdoors, titanium has largely replaced yesterday's lead and zinc. Indoors, new alkyd resins and rubber bases have largely replaced yesterday's oils. Today's paints go on easier, cover more area per gallon, weather better, wash better, stay white longer, offer more colors, stay sunfast, and some even smell better. They are easier to repaint and, relatively speaking, they cost less.

Outdoors, titanium makes today's white paints chalk faster and more uniformly and thus retain their whiteness better against fumes and soot. They crack and chip less than yesterday's lead and zinc paints, accumulate less dirt, and therefore require less labor in preparing them for repainting. They can be covered over with new one-coat paints (more accurately called "repaint whites") which dry with a high luster.

New colorants permit many more sunfast outdoor colors. New

synthetic resins and powders permit accent colors that retain their brilliance and luster, with new nonchalking varieties of titanium helping to maintain the color.

Also available are new stains of greater color permanence and greater color variety, new flat paints with great color stability for shingles, and new special paints for masonry and stucco.

Indoors, the new alkyd flats produce a more durable finish with better washability and better color and gloss retention. New latex paints can be thinned with water and applied very easily with brush or roller coater where their high gloss is not an objection and a wide variety of colors is not needed. These latex paints are hard to beat for long wear and washability, and on exterior walls they do double duty as a vapor seal. A recent paint in this bright new line is jelled pain. Jelled paint is thixotropic—it sits in a sullen blob until it is attacked with brush or roller. Jelled paint needs no mixing, won't drip, and doesn't spill should you kick over the can.

BUT THE PAINTERS COST MORE

Paint is cheap, but painting is expensive. Labor costs for painting run five to ten times as high as material costs. Painters' wages, since World War II, have climbed more than those of almost any other trade. The high cost of painting is a matter not only of high wages but also of conservatism and refusal to take advantage of new methods and materials to increase the productivity of the painter. A case in point, often cited, is the insistence on using a narrow brush although almost all of today's paints flow so easily that there is little reason why wide brushes should not be used.

Whether because of high costs for painters' services or because today's ready mixed paints make painting so easy, 75 per cent of all interior painting is now do-it-yourself by amateurs. Thirty years ago, painters had to mix their own paints. Most paints then were "professional paints"—that is, they had to be mixed by a professional. But now you can get a much better job by

221

using paint just as it comes from the can. In fact, one of the builders' biggest headaches is the way painters adulterate good paint on the pretext of improving it. Many smart builders buy their own paint to discourage this adulteration. They get the same trade discount as the painter, and good paint costs so little that it is foolish to buy a cheaper grade. Some builders even use a hydrometer to catch adulteration and ration the turpentine they allow for washing up (for fear it might be used to thin the paint).

Paint can be applied at the factory for about one-fourth as much as at the site, usually by spraying or dipping. Therefore all building parts and components which will need paint—including, specifically, window frames, sashes, doors, siding, and perhaps shingles—should be given an invisible primer coat in the factory and also a neutral second coat (white if the third coat is to be a lighter color, gray if it is to be darker).

This would not only cut in half the labor cost of painting, it would also get the job done sooner; builders no longer have to wait for dry weather to start painting.

HELPFUL HINTS
FOR PAINT MANUFACTURERS

Let the builders know. The makers of paints have only themselves to blame if so few builders realize how much paint products have been improved. Manufacturers have been so busy selling their product to consumers they have not kept communications open in the trade channels through which those products must reach the consumers. They have not merchandised their better products to the building industry.

For the past twenty years many architects and builders have tried to minimize painted areas, believing that the less paint they used the less the upkeep would be. More houses would have larger painted areas if paint manufacturers had told builders what they were doing to cut both the first cost and the maintenance cost of paint.

222

Stop neglecting the new-house market. It is foolish for paint manufacturers to neglect the new-house market. The troubles of the wallpaper industry began only when it let wallpaper go out of style in new construction. In any one year paint sales may well be five times as great for repainting the old as for painting the new, but it must be remembered that the new house sets the fashion. Almost by definition, modernizing means making old houses look like new houses.

One of the very best ways to sell more paint for old houses is to encourage more and better use of new products in the new-house market, for soon the owners of old houses will begin buying paint to copy whatever style the new house sets. The merchant-builder's model house, visited by thousands of lookers every weekend, is the best showroom manufacturers could ask. One big reason the appliance makers are eager to sell color into the kitchen is their hope that colored kitchens in new houses will also start a big replacement demand as old houses follow the new-house lead. That's why General Electric is so pleased that up to 25 per cent of its new-house major-appliance sales are in color.

Make sure you are selling to your real customer. In the new-house market the consumer is not the most important person to sell, for most new houses are painted before anyone knows who will buy them. The ultimate judge of color may be the consumer—the person who buys the house. But before paint manufacturers can sell color to the consumer they must first sell to the builder, who must sell it to his mortgage lender and his appraiser before he can even start building the house, The consumer is no more important than the architect whose choice of materials fixes how big or how small the painted areas will be. The consumer is no more important than the builder, who on five houses out of six picks the colors and buys the paint before he has any idea who will buy the house. The consumer is no more important than the mortgage lender, who put far more money into the house than the buyer, and no more important than the appraiser who guides the lender's decision.

223

Make it easy for builders to use color well. Provide professional color advisory service. Manufacturers should realize the builder must learn more about color and take more responsibility for color. They would be smart to recognize that the builder is busy, and color is only one of many subjects with which he must increasingly be concerned. Few builders will give color a top priority on their time. They are too harassed by such growing problems as where to get land, where to get mortgage money, how to get community facilities.

Manufacturers who would exploit the use of more and better color could profit by the experience of the manufacturers who sought to exploit the use of more and better lighting. For years they promoted the infinite variety available in lighting and found they were getting nowhere. But sales began to rise when they switched their emphasis from variety to simplicity and focused their promotion on just twenty-one ways to profit by better illumination. The auto industry put seventy million cars on our streets by making those cars increasingly simple to drive.

WALLPAPER AND THE NEW–HOUSE MARKET

Wallpaper and/or vinyl plastic wall covering are good ways to color walls. These materials give the builder an exceptionally flexible color choice. With factory-applied design, texture, and color, wallpaper was, in fact, just about the first prefabricated component offered to the building industry. Its quantity production makes economical many vari-colored effects no builder can afford to create with paint.

For a time the wallpaper industry seemed likely to provide a classic example of how to lose the replacement market by neglecting the new-house market, which, though smaller, sets the style. But now wallpaper is staging a comeback with new promotions and new designs that suit today's new houses.

A generation ago most rooms were papered, with the same paper used on all four walls. Today, patterned papers are used mostly for accent on a single wall, with the other walls either painted or covered by a plainer paper. Good color combinations for this use of two papers in the same room are worked out and recommended by the makers. Some wallpapers are sold with matching colors in draperies and paint.

THE WONDROUS NEW WALLS

Even as the paint manufacturers continue to improve their product, new and colorful materials now poking up over the building horizon may help make paint obsolete.

To date, the most important of these new materials have been the colored metals. Panels of steel, aluminum, or laminated metal are covered with a colorful and durable ceramic or plastic coat. Some aluminum panels are anodized. The new panels are light, strong, and easy to erect—manufacturers claim that the thermal efficiency of some of the panels is three times better than eight inches of masonry.

At present most of the new metal skins are going on industrial and office buildings. The demand is heavy—in 1956 there was a $40-million market for the new materials. The panels are used inside and out; since they supply a building "skin," rather than a bearing wall, lightness is one of their chief virtues.

The new panels take easily to color. Varicolored glazes brighten the steel panels; vinyl coatings in a myriad of colors and textures bond to nonferrous metals; aluminum is blossoming forth in a host of new shades, including a handsome sea green. Finishes are matt, luster, or semiluster. Inevitably, the new panels are going to make their impact felt on the home builder, especially now that U.S. Steel Homes offers light, easy-to-assemble steel frames.

The manufacturer of building materials and the builders are still left holding a colorful tiger by the tail: with an almost limitless range of colors to draw from, what colors should the manufacturer make and the builder buy? Again, with his buyers largely unknown and with the unlikelihood in the new media of changing the color of a house once it is up, the builder is

225

going to do well to stick to safe and compatible colors—colors for which there is a predictable demand. And these are clearly the colors the manufacturer should make. Color engineering is going to have a lot of work to do when builders begin bolting colorful metal walls to the frame of America's homes.

The metal-panel manufacturers are already running into competition. They are casting a nervous eye toward, of all places, Disneyland. For there, in Tomorrowland, is Monsanto's pioneer plastic House of Tomorrow. Fireproof, durable, and permanently colored, this cruciform dwelling uses paired plastic modules for its four wings, cantilevered from a central core that houses kitchen, bath, laundry, and heating facilities. Transparent shatterproof plastic panels serve as windows. Built-in plastic insulation—Monsanto claims it is equivalent to 9½ feet of concrete in resisting heat flow—makes the house cooler in the summer and warmer in the winter.

Monsanto's house is a prototype; there will not be one in your neighborhood next week. But Monsanto has done some cost figuring, and estimates that similar plastic houses could be mass-produced in the 1959 market at prices under $25,000. That means the plastic house is with us. One of the greatest increases in the already skyrocketing use of color has been in plastics; the impact of the plastic house on the home builder's, financer's, and planner's color problems is obvious. Plastic colors are bonded right into the material. Once a plastic wall is up it will stay up. The plastic house will probably represent the ultimate in color preselection, both by manufacturer and builder. The commercial success of the house may well depend on the skill and authority of that selection.

COLOR PREFERENCES OF HOME OWNERS

The color preferences of home owners and home buyers must be taken into account in resolving the pull-and-haul among builders, appliance manufacturers, financers, and all the other people who look toward the home buyer as their ultimate customer. The Philip Carey Manufacturing Company has reported some facts about these color preferences that may be surprising.

In roofing and in house paint thirteen especially effective colors constitute the vast majority of sales—even though roofing manufacturers offer a total of more than 850 colors and paint manufacturers more than 1,300 (with the chance to mix an infinitely greater number). Among all this vast choice, white has been and is the number one choice both in roofing and in exterior house paint!

Here are the top preferences for 1958:

RANK	ROOFING	EXTERIOR HOUSE PAINT
1	White	White 44 per cent
2	Green	Green * 16 per cent
3	Red	Yellows 11 per cent
4	Black	Red † 8 per cent
5	Gray	Gray 6 per cent
6	Tan, Brown, Orange	Blues 5 per cent

COLOR ADVICE FOR HOME BUILDERS

Here is a check list of some elementary advice all builders can profit by materially:

1. People tend to like the familiar color combinations. Just about the safest color combinations are those we see all the time in nature.

2. Don't try so hard to get colors to match. It is usually impossible to match colors in different materials, and often difficult even in the same material.

3. Don't use colors so nearly alike that the eye is not sure at a glance whether or not they are meant to match.

4. Don't do any room all in one color—not even a kitchen or a bath. Most rooms will be most pleasant if at least four compatible colors are used, one of them an accent color.

5. Use the same color in adjoining rooms to borrow space

* Light and medium green.
† Strong on the West Coast.

and make small rooms seem larger. For example, if the bedrooms are small, paint them and the hall the same color.

6. Color harmony depends not only on the colors used but also on the absolute and relative size of the areas covered with each color. People can stand only so much area of bright colors. A beautiful mosaic enlarged ten times becomes garish. A small spot of bright red against a gray background is much more pleasing than a small gray spot against a bright red background.

7. Small amounts of lightness-contrast are the easiest harmonies. Strong contrasts should be ventured only with expert guidance.

8. Remember that neutral colors make the best background for a greater variety of special treatment.

9. The two safest colors to use are a neutral gray and a beige, with buff preferable when a good deal of natural wood will show. Either of these colors will make a good background against which many other colors can be used as accents.

10. When in doubt, use light gray. It harmonizes well as a background for any color.

11. Use neutral colors to make a room seem bigger. Any strong color makes the walls seem nearer. You can create emotional spaciousness with light colors.

12. Never use strong colors for large areas where they will be hard to change. Colors that catch the eye in a showroom are not always colors people would want to live with.

13. Don't sell white short as a color. It is still one of the very best.

14. Don't hesitate to use lighter colors on the floor. They help reflect light advantageously.

15. Remember that dark colors—especially as their gloss increases—tend to show up any imperfections in your walls and ceiling.

16. Try to put on the wall opposite the window any dark or saturated colors you use for impact. But even these should usually have a reflectance of 40 per cent or better.

17. Remember dark outside colors absorb sun heat and make the house harder to cool. The roof is the worst place to use dark colors, for the roof gets the most sun radiation; more than half the new houses are being roofed in white.

18. Don't expect dark exterior paints to weather as well as lighter ones.

19. Remember that color and light are inseparable; colors change when the light changes. Don't settle your choice on any color combinations until you have seen them in the light under which the colors are to be used.

20. Use light colors for counter tops, especially in bath and kitchen. Their reflections are an important part of your lighting system; they provide the lighting from below. Pink reflected light is the most flattering.

21. Don't use ordinary fluorescent lamps in a color kitchen. They will change all the colors, which are usually designed to look right under daylight. Use cool white lamps instead.

22. Exterior color harmony along the street is as important as color harmony on the individual house. It gives the buyer his first impression of a development. The smaller the lot is, the more important this color harmony becomes. The more alike the houses are, the more important it is to get good variety in their color.

23. Don't upset a good color harmony just to get a better price on some item. If the price bargain is too good to pass up, a color engineer should review the whole color scheme.

24. For kitchen walls, light or medium tones of color are best because they reflect the most light and provide the best background for equipment and accessories. Some of the most satisfactory wall colors are yellow, yellow-green, yellowish gray, apple green, bluish green, buff, and turquoise. Have ceilings lighter than the walls, using pale pink, ivory, white, or a tint of the wall color. If the ceiling is low, white is the best color to give height. Use your bright accents for furniture, interior of cupboards, and accessories.

25. Respect public color preferences in your vicinity.

229

COLOR FOR INTERIOR DECORATION

In the last chapter we looked at the problems that builders, mortgagors, and manufacturers have been facing in picking the basic home colors—roofing, siding, wall finishes.

How about color for home decoration? Do the businessman and manufacturer have any worries there? Of course they do. The builder of the housing development finds himself squarely faced with interior-decorating problems when he puts up that model house—the house which is going to decide just how many of his other houses he sells. The apartment-house owner worries about color every time he redecorates or furnishes an apartment. The manufacturer of furniture, the designer of draperies, the home-appliance company—all of these are directly concerned with the problem of how to use color correctly in decorating the home.

WHAT COLOR CAN DO FOR YOU

A beautifully proportioned room or piece of furniture can be made even more pleasing through the proper use of color.

The wrong color arrangement can obliterate those proportions. The builder of a model home might be attracted to a catalogue's illustration of a breakfront bookcase, for example. Moreover the breakfront is scaled to fit a certain wall space which the builder is worried about. It is well proportioned and its detail is excellent. "I'll order it in black," says the builder, "and take care of that pesky wall." The wall, regrettably, is light blue; in goes the breakfront and out it leaps from the wall—it somehow seems all out of proportion for the room and for the space it was meant to go in.

Next on the builder's list is a cabinet—handsomely carved, full of fine detail. "I'll have it stained dark mahogany," says the builder. "Just the thing to give it that antique look." Just the thing to obliterate all that fine detail, too. A highlighted finish would have brought out the carving; so would the careful staining of deeper tones in the shadows to emphasize the highlights.

It has been truly said that color is the most attractive and the most dangerous element that enters the decorative scheme of any room. In the hands of the layman—or of the color-unconscious builder above—color can be dangerous. The builder would certainly hesitate to start throwing up rafters without the preliminary work of an architect. But arm him with a dozen decorating magazines and he is indeed on his evil way to buying a host of colors which may at best antagonize his customers and at worst prevent him from having any customers at all.

Let's consider the function of color in the home. In the dining room, for example, colors should stimulate and aid digestion. So the *function* of this room certainly should be considered in the selection of colors. A boy's bedroom is quite a different matter from the living room of a sophisticated hostess, and not only the furniture but the *colors* can point up the difference. Point one: color must be functional.

Point two is that color must be suitable. White is fine in certain rooms—but it just does not belong on furniture if there are going to be dogs or young children in the house. Pastel hues do not fit in a wood-paneled den, and there are other less obvious situations where the colors selected are not always suitable for the use to which they are put.

In this day of cramped living quarters no wise builder wants to make a room look smaller than it is, so that problem isn't worth considering. But we often want to make a room look larger or another shape, to raise the apparent height of a ceiling, for example. Color can do that. It is amazing how much nearer your head seems to a gun-metal gray ceiling than to the same ceiling painted a pale sky-blue.

Proportion, too, can be altered by the intelligent use of color. The long, narrow room can be shortened by using strong color at the ends. The square room can be given more interesting conformation by using color in corners or in panels, or as emphasis for the fireplace or the windows.

Color can easily give a room the character which it may lack, architecturally speaking. Any variation of mood or temperament can be induced by employing the proper colors in the surroundings. For instance, you can "air condition" with cool colors, and warm a room with warm colors! You can even "sleep condition" a room. One measure that persons suffering from sleeplessness might employ advantageously would be to use a dark color (certain deep blues, perhaps) on the wall they face while lying in bed. This might help to insure longer rest at dusk or dawn, when the sun's rays invading the bedroom would be absorbed by the dark surface and be kept from striking the eyes.

WHICH COLORS TO USE?

Now consider some of the places where color plays an important part in home and apartment decoration, and what those colors should be. Unless the color emphasis has been placed elsewhere, it is the walls and the windows which we see first when entering a room. If it is daylight, the eye reaches quickly to the window no matter how strong the wall color. If it is nighttime and the artificial illumination is properly and evenly balanced, the most obvious light source may attract the eye first, but the usual focal interest centers on the *walls*. The color of the wall paint, then, is vitally important. Never fail to choose a wall color that is part of your basic color scheme— whether it's monochromatic, related, or complementary.

Green hues are still favorites for walls, maybe because these tones wear well, make an excellent background for wood furniture in anything from dark mahogany to the lightest natural finish, and give scope for bright accents of color. Three of the most popular tonings are deep forest green with a bluish cast, light yellow-green, and a medium gray-green.

Pink, formerly considered a color that could only be used in a bedroom, has now spread its influence and is seen in living room, dining room, and kitchen as well. One of the great advantages of pink is that it is flattering to women (and women have lots to say when it comes to buying that new house). It also allies well with any style of furnishings, from Victorian to Modern. Combined, for interest, with warm gray, medium-light bottle green, and darker-blue plum, it adds up to an interior color scheme that is harmonious and intensely feminine without being anemic.

Soft plum is a color that can be used with excellent effect with modern furniture. Aquamarine walls give a cool look to a room with a southern exposure. Coral-colored walls give welcoming warmth to a hallway, especially when contrasted with floor covering and woodwork in the beige-to-grayish-brown range.

COLOR SUGGESTIONS
FOR FOYERS IN SMALL HOMES

1. Papered walls—using wallpaper with a white ground and a large but simple floral design in gray, black, and emerald green
   Ceiling—white; also all woodwork except doors

Doors—emerald green

Rug—black

This treatment is dramatic but not overpowering. The light walls and woodwork make the area appear larger. The simplicity of the color scheme keeps it in harmony with many decorative plans for the rooms opening out of the vestibule.

2. Walls—cork beige. This can be paint but would be more interesting in a textured wall covering such as vinyl strawtex in natural beige or a real cork laminate.

Ceiling and woodwork, including doors—light, clear lemon yellow

Floor—random cork tile

This is a warm and friendly color arrangement consisting of only two closely related colors. It can serve as an introduction to rooms in similar hues, such as brown, gold or rust, or as a contrasting accent for rooms decorated in quite different colors.

3. Walls—oyster white

Woodwork, including doors—light gray in a shade harmonizing with and only slightly darker than the wall color

Ceiling—coral

Rug—coral

This plan is excellent for a small vestibule in which the ceiling is disproportionately high. The warm, fairly bright ceiling and floor make these areas appear closer together, whereas the light, neutral color of walls and woodwork seems to push these apart and extend them.

4. Walls—papered with a wallpaper in a small, unobtrusive geometric design in white and silver

Ceiling—any medium-light shade of blue. This can be turquoise or violet-blue or cerulean.

Woodwork and doors—silver gray

Rug—silver gray

A treatment such as this is recommended for a very small area having a low ceiling. The blue distance color seems to push the ceiling upward and the off-white walls look farther away than they are.

WINDOW TREATMENT

Next to the walls in order of color importance are the draperies, which call attention to the windows and are often the major wall decoration. In using draperies of patterned fabric, it is wise to match the wall color to a dominant shade in the draperies; a fabric in gray, white, and yellow, against gray walls and with a yellow rug, sets a pleasant harmony in a living-room décor.

At the windows, too, the light may be tempered by strongly colored curtains. Where there is no sunshine and not too much light, a strong yellow-gold curtain will add a lighthearted, summery atmosphere to the room. But this cannot be used if that particular quality of yellow fights with the other colors in the scheme. When the light is too strong for the rest and repose that seem necessary in a bedroom, the light can be softened with curtains of gray or pale aquamarine. If it is warmth that the room needs there is always the friendly and becoming shell or flesh pink to use for draperies.

FLOORS

Next, consider the floor, which is certainly the second-largest area of color in any room. There we have the problem of plain color versus pattern, but mostly the question is color. There are rugs which occupy the center of the floor area or there are wall-to-wall carpets which give the floor a more unified and architectural treatment. There are the hard floor coverings which are every day growing more colorful—the different varieties of asphalt, vinyl, linoleum, rubber, cork. All of these can be used to enrich a room's color personality.

Since wall-to-wall carpeting is likely to be the most expensive single color component of any room, it will usually be a fixed feature through several repaintings or repaperings and changes of furniture. Hence a neutral shade—even gray or beige—is likely to prove most practical.

FURNITURE

Another of the color planner's preoccupations is furniture. Furniture color is a primary concern for manufacturer and builder—as well as for the furniture dealer. We tend to think of mahogany or walnut or maple or oak as a real or simulated wood, but it is color nevertheless, and as such must be blended harmoniously into the color ensemble of the room. A red mahogany has to be handled one way and a brown mahogany another. A fine mellow maple is one of the most delightful and livable of color tones, but red maple needs to be placed with great care and skill or it can ruin an otherwise attractive room. Painted furniture, of which there is a great deal, and metal furniture provide still other colors to be considered with the ensemble in color planning.

It is interesting to note, in this connection, that the very latest trends in furniture colors are to simplicity—simplicity of colors to match the simplicity of design that has become so popular in this generation. Just as today's home buyers and apartment leasers don't want unnecessarily ornamented furniture, so are they also rejecting unnecessary or tawdry colors on their furniture. Quite a change from the rather ornate colors of the 1920's.

Today, everything on furniture, including the colors, must have a *reason* for being there. Hence, the trend to fewer and more truly functional furniture colors. And speaking of actual trends in color, it is to be noted that the darker finishes for furniture are growing in demand.

Don't buy a chair or a sofa merely because you want something to sit on. This is a good reason, but you should first consider whether it helps carry out the color theme of the room. Or it may be that you need a bright contrasting accent in one corner.

236

A clever colorist may be able to mix pink and orange successfully, but it takes a lot of know-how to do so. Let the requirements of the room be your guide. A small room with a high ceiling facing north needs light, warm shades such as yellow or peach. Don't worry too much about cleaning problems. Today most paints and fabrics are fairly easy to clean. So you can use a pale color for your floor if it is required.

It is best not to have more than three basic colors in one room and these should be repeated in more than one place for balance. But you needn't confine yourself to a single shade or intensity of each color. There are many gradations that look well together and give you pleasant variations.

Use only one outstanding pattern, whether a floral print, an outlandish modern rug or a "busy" drapery fabric.

ACCESSORIES

Lastly, we come to the accessories—those items which can add personality and the individual touch to a room. They include such things as sofa cushions and footstools, colored telephones, vases and cigarette boxes, ash trays, flowers and plants, lamps and shades—even an odd chair. That's quite a formidable array and a most important one. It's a safe rule to say that vivid color touches *can* be best introduced in these items. Furthermore, in rooms decorated in basically neutral tones, the entire character can be altered merely by changing the accessories. But never forget that these small, bright color notes can provide an excellent complement to a color scheme *or* put it out of key. Here again, it is wise to take the advice of a skilled color planner, or to follow such basic rules as accenting a grayed color scheme with a touch of pure color, or a cold color scheme with a touch of warm color.

Lampshades are sometimes a tricky factor in a room plan. Take, for instance, the room which needs a highlight of blue in one corner. A clear blue lampshide fills the bill perfectly—by day. But by night, that particular lamp might produce a blue light, slightly grayed, and probably would not help the color scheme one bit.

COLOR HINTS FOR HOME PLANNERS

In this era, with design improving all the time in every field of mass-produced furniture and furnishings, one can rely on simplicity in color groupings. Simplicity and carefully harmonized color schemes are more important than ever, good twin targets for the manufacturer, builder, designer, and planner to shoot for.

All color combinations can be reduced, at root, to three basic arrangements: matching, harmonizing, and contrasting schemes. Within each of these, there is endless room for individual expression.

A *matching scheme* uses various tints, shades, and grayed tones of a single color. If the color is yellow, for example, the basic shade preferred can be combined with several other shades ranging from cream, buff, or beige yellows to those with an umber cast. It may be accented with metallic gold. The use of a single color need never be monotonous if it includes dramatic contrasts of dark and light with accents of pure, clear color.

A *harmonizing scheme* uses colors which are closely related, such as rose, violet, and plum, or chartreuse and forest green. These in-between colors gain interest by variations in darkness and lightness as well as in intensity. Further variations are created by mixing smooth and rough fabrics and finishes which, although the same shade, will appear lighter or darker because of the amount of light they reflect. Either matching or harmonizing schemes are restful.

A *contrasting scheme,* using pairs of colors which are direct opposites on the color wheel—such as yellow and violet—achieves more excitement in a room. Obviously, such combinations must be handled with care or the result will be overwhelming. It is best to let one of the two colors dominate and to be sufficiently gray, or lighten one or both so that they do not clash.

238

While too much harmony can be cloying, violently contrasting colors create nervous tension.

When considering colors for home decoration, remember also that traditionally colors have symbolism.

COLOR AND LIGHT IN THE HOME

Artificial illumination has so much effect on how well a color scheme appears that it must be considered at length. Too often a room is designed only for daylight but is used chiefly during the hours when artificial light is necessary. The careful color planner has to work out the problem of hours-of-use before any color scheme is completed. And he must plan colors to look their best under all varieties of light.

Bear in mind that what you see as color in a room is the combined influence of the light source, the surrounding colors, and the color of the object you see. There are as many different colors as there are kinds of light in which an object can be seen. Two fabrics that appear to be the identical shade when exposed to ordinary daylight may look like two different colors under an incandescent lamp. Under incandescent light, for instance, navy or midnight blue will look black. I have seen bathroom installations where the color appearance of tile near the window is totally different in shade and hue from that of the same tiles on another wall illuminated by incandescent light.

Light plays other tricks, too. It can be used to enhance, rather than to dull and distort colors, and by changing the colors only slightly, light can make the difference between a warm or cold, bright or depressing, relaxing or exciting, attractive or uninviting room.

One simple way to change interior lighting effects is to use a tinted filter adapted to fit over light sources. The colored-glass filter or gelatin which most nearly matches the color to be accented gives the best results and creates a subdued, dramatic glow. If a filter of a contrasting (complementary) color is used, the color to be accented will be deadened instead, or even made to appear gray. (Reddish light makes a blue surface appear reddish gray; greenish light makes a purple surface appear grayish brown; and blue light tends to neutralize yellow, etc.)

WHICH TYPE OF LIGHT?

In their effects on color, fluorescent lights differ one from another almost as much as they do from incandescent light. The best type of lighting for most of the home builder's uses is the cool-white fluorescent lamp, which will bring out the true color of furnishings with a minimum of distortion. For a perfectly white light source, install cool-white fluorescent lighting with a warm-tone (pink) paint or enamel finish on the deflector. This warm tone, which may also be used on the ceiling, will impart the right degree of color correction, and under the resultant white light all colors will look natural and unchanged, just as they appear at midmorning on a clear spring day.

The former universal use of incandescent lamps greatly emphasized yellows and reds, but now fluorescent-light sources bring emphasis to the blues and greens. This assures richer and more satisfying color harmony. Research on the effects of fluorescent illumination on color rendition has resulted in charts for predicting the changes in a color as it is moved from one light source to another. These should be of practical value to the home builder, interior decorator, and the manufacturer in helping them visualize the actual appearance of the color they choose for walls, rugs, draperies, upholstery, and the like, under different typical light sources.

HOW TO SAY "WELCOME"

One final point: Consider the inadequacy of the usual entrance-hall light. Sometimes the hallway is so dim that even the host cannot be sure who is entering the door. If the entrance hall is supposed to set the keynote for the house, why not let it be one of welcome—not of subdued tones which seem to indicate unfriendliness? With the right light and color plan you can say a cordial welcome even in a small hall.

240

COLOR COMMENTS

More Heat from Your Radiators

The United States Department of Agriculture suggests that the careful selection of paint color for your radiator may save considerably on the cost of fuel bills.

Metallic paints, such as bronze or aluminum, cut down the amount of heat as does a shiny white. This is because these paints give the radiator a bright shiny surface, which reflects the heat inward as well as outward, preventing full radiation. In contrast, a flat paint with some color in it will improve the heating efficiency of the radiator.

Generally, the darker the color of the radiator, the more heat will be given off. If a dark shade of flat paint, to harmonize with the room color is chosen, the radiators will be both efficient and inconspicuous.

A Blotter to Help the Painter

To determine the color rubber-base paint will be when it is dry, apply a smooth coat of paint to a clean white blotter. The blotter absorbs the liquid, leaving only the dry pigment on the surface.

Some Paint Colors Have Limitations

COLOR	CANNOT BE MADE	REASON
Gray	More orange	Adding orange to gray makes beige, a different hue
Blue	More orange, yellower, browner	Complementary and approximately complementary colors gray each other.
Green	Redder, more orange	Approximately complementary colors gray each other.
Red	Greener	Complementary colors gray each other.
Orange	Bluer, greener	Complementary and approximately complementary colors gray each other.
Yellow	Bluer, violet	Adding blue to yellow produces green. Adding yellow to violet produces gray.

COLOR IN NATIONAL DEFENSE — CAMOUFLAGE

This book deals with color planning for business and industry, and national defense is currently the biggest industry in the United States. So far we've touched on some of the peripheral (and not so peripheral) defense uses of color: the Navy's habitability program, the Air Force's experiments in improving aircraft conspicuity, the Department of Defense's incorporation of color planning in its new building. Another is in the ancient and honorable art of camouflage.

Camouflage has come a long way since Genghis Khan poked shrubbery into the battle dress of his warriors and Julius Caesar daubed the upper works of his galleys blue. In the eighteenth and nineteenth centuries the camoufleur worried about the two-dimensional environment of land warfare—Rogers' Rangers prowled the shores of Lake Champlain in green uniforms; the Boer War took Her Majesty's troops out of red coats into khaki. By the twentieth century the airplane had brought a third dimension into the picture. World War I roads hid from observation balloons under cloth-garnished fish nets and World War

242

I warships wore piebald dazzle camouflage to make U-boat skippers boggle their estimate of target angle.

By World War II a host of new photography techniques was making life still more difficult for the camoufleur. Infrared photography saw through paint. The stereoscopic camera and the morning-and-afternoon shadow pair picked out dummy structures. The camoufleur retaliated with new paints, more lifelike dummies, and with wholesale modifications of terrain— the Germans kept British bombers away from a crucial Hamburg dock area for several raids by rafting over part of the harbor so it looked like land and constructing a fake breakwater so that part of an estuary looked like the harbor.

Now the camoufleur has more troubles still. Nuclear weapons have eliminated the necessity for pin-point bombing; a nuclear bomb falling two miles away from your installation will knock it out just as effectively as one coming in the window. Guided missiles, navigating by radar or by the stars and seeking their targets by heat or sound, are now in business. They are singularly insensitive to many of the visual forms of camouflage as we now know it.

But there still is a place for camouflage, even in the jet-propelled and nuclear-armed environment of today's war, and for two reasons:

Camouflage can make life miserable for the targeter. No matter how sophisticated the guided missile you may be planning to launch, you still have to know where to launch it. The military calls the process of locating that place targeting, and by obscuring his prospective target, camouflage can cross up the man who draws the target map.

Camouflage has considerable value in brush-fire wars. Even if the missile director knows where to shoot, there's no certainty that he's going to. On the contrary, a large part of our defense program today is tailored to the concept that nobody can afford to fight a nuclear war; that if there are future wars, they will be local, Korea-type conflicts, fought in conventional ways with conventional arms. Camouflage was very much in business in the conventional warfare of World War II, and it will equally be in business in any conventional war in the future.

HOW CAMOUFLAGE WORKS

Camouflage is a French word, rooted in the verb *camoufler,* "to disguise." That's what camouflage does. It does this through three techniques: concealment, changing identity, and decoying.

Concealment. This is the most conventional camouflage technique. It is involved in the Marine's multicolored jungle uniform, in the garnished net strung across the airplane on the ground or over the factory, in the olive drab paint job on the artillery observation plane. Concealment, self-evidently, tries to prevent the enemy from seeing what you don't want him to see.

Change in identity. Some things are too big or too awkward to conceal. In that case we don't try to hide them but to make them look like something else. The German reconstruction of Hamburg's harbor was an example of change in identity. So was the light aircraft carrier the Japanese sent steaming into the Leyte Gulf fight in 1944 with its flight deck painted to make it look like a cruiser. The commerce-raiding German merchant cruisers of both wars were professional impostors; they were fitted with dummy funnels and collapsible deckhouses and they repainted at sea in their concentrated efforts to change their identity. The Douglas aircraft plant at Santa Monica was still another World War II example of this technique. It was painted and netted to simulate a farm, with simulated cows grazing and unsimulated clothes fluttering on genuine clotheslines on its roof.

Decoying. Sometimes it's impossible to conceal or disguise a target. Then the camoufleur tries to draw the enemy to another target altogether. To this end the British Army in its Western Europe campaign went around inflating remarkably lifelike

244

rubber reproductions of tanks, vehicles, aircraft, and even landing barges. The Germans constructed entire synthetic villages and factories to draw Allied bombing raids. More recently the Egyptians claimed to have drawn the teeth of Anglo-French bombing raids with wooden reproductions of airplanes, although photographic evidence indicates that the Egyptians used not dummies but the burned-out shells of planes which somehow never quite got off the ground.

TOOLS OF THE CAMOUFLEUR

The camoufleur hides, changes, or decoys through modifications of color, shape, and texture. In performing these modifications, he draws on a set of tools that are familiar indeed to the color engineer. Let's look at some of them.

Color

The camouflage engineer puts color to work in various ways. The obvious way is through paint; some of the less obvious ways are through strips of cloth strung on a net, or through natural colors—actual earth or shrubbery, for example.

One of the camouflage engineer's first problems is to select color vehicles which will be effective on the wide variety of surfaces he must color. Here are some of the most useful vehicles:

SURFACE	VEHICLE
Turf	Casein cold-water paint, and bituminous paints
Cement	Bituminous emulsion
Cloth	Oleo-resinous emulsion or cold-water paint
Concrete Wood Metal Glass	Dull oil paint
Earth and gravel	Tar

245

This is only the first problem, however. Even tougher is developing colors which will do the job—colors which will fool both the eye and the perspicacious gaze of the aerial camera. In my work in camouflage I've developed a series of colors which fulfill this double job. These colors are listed here with their ingredients. Note that they can be made in two ways. In the *pigment-mixture method* the component paints are physically mixed in the proportion indicated. In the *visual-blend method* the pigments are left pure and painted on in small separate areas (like the color blobs on the camouflage ponchos the Marines used to wear); the colors will appear to blend together a short distance away, and, with the percentage of each pigment's area equal to the part relationships in the second column, will produce the desired hue.

GREEN NO. 1

COMPONENT COLORS	PIGMENT MIXTURE	VISUAL BLEND
Permanent Green	12 parts	25%
Blue-Black	3 parts	35%
Georgia Ocher	2 parts	
Ferrite Red	2 parts	
Metallic Brown		40%

GREEN NO. 2

COMPONENT COLORS	PIGMENT MIXTURE	VISUAL BLEND
Permanent Green	8 parts	20.5%
Georgia Ocher	8 parts	
Ferrite Red	1 part	2 %
Blue-Black		67 %
Lemon Ferrite		10.5%

GREEN NO. 3

Permanent Green (basic color—no mixture or blending of components required)

GREEN NO. 4

COMPONENT COLORS	PIGMENT MIXTURE	VISUAL BLEND
Permanent Green	10 parts	77%
Lemon Ferrite	6 parts	23%

246

RED NO. 1

Metallic (basic color—no mixture or blending of components required)

RED NO. 2

COMPONENT COLORS	PIGMENT MIXTURE	VISUAL BLEND
Ferrite Red	8 parts	74%
Georgia Ocher	7 parts	10%
Permanent Green	5 parts	16%

RED NO. 3

Ferrite Red (basic color—no mixture or blending of components required)

RED NO. 4

COMPONENT COLORS	PIGMENT MIXTURE	VISUAL BLEND
Lemon Ferrite	1 part	45%
Ferrite Red	1 part	29%
White	10 parts	26%

BROWN NO. 1

Raw Umber (basic color—no mixture or blending of components required)

BROWN NO. 2

COMPONENT COLORS	PIGMENT MIXTURE	VISUAL BLEND
Georgia Ocher	15 parts	23%
Metallic Brown	12 parts	77%
White	2 parts	

BROWN NO. 3

COMPONENT COLORS	PIGMENT MIXTURE	VISUAL BLEND
Georgia Ocher	10 parts	30%
Raw Umber	7 parts	70%
White	2 parts	

BROWN NO. 4

Georgia Ocher (basic color—no mixture or blending of components required)

GRAY NO. 1

COMPONENT COLORS	PIGMENT MIXTURE	VISUAL BLEND
Permanent Green	15 parts	6%
White	5 parts	6%
Blue-Black	4 parts	83%
Ferrite Red	3 parts	5%

247

GRAY NO. 2

COMPONENT COLORS	PIGMENT MIXTURE	VISUAL BLEND
Blue-Black	7 parts	75%
White	5 parts	25%

GRAY NO. 3

COMPONENT COLORS	PIGMENT MIXTURE	VISUAL BLEND
Permanent Green	6 parts	49%
White	4 parts	15%
Ferrite Red	1 part	36%
Georgia Ocher	1 part	

These colors find ready use in the camouflage business. For example, patterns to blend an installation with its surroundings may be readily made by painting. No colors need appear in pattern areas which scale less than fifty feet; patterns tend to cancel out if they are used in smaller scale. All patterns must be colored to suit the surroundings, of course. The green foliage of deciduous trees, with its chlorophyll content, reflects much of the infrared light back into certain types of high aerial cameras. Leaf-bearing trees therefore look white on infrared photos. On the other hand, coniferous trees, such as the spruces and pines, have little infrared reflectivity and their evergreen needles show dark in photographs. Consequently paints used to simulate the types of nearby trees or to blend in with them must be compatible with those trees.

Texture

Texture is often even more important than color in camouflage. The wrong texture is more of a dead giveaway in reconnaissance photographs than the wrong color choice. Texture determines far more than color whether an area will appear light or dark, for example. A smooth black tarred surface will appear lighter than a patch of light green woodland. The key is the light-absorbing quality of the surface, and rough-textured surfaces absorb more light and look darker than smooth ones.

Among the reliable textural materials the camoufleur uses are sand, cottonseed hulls, sawdust, and tanbark—all colorable with bituminous emulsion. Black steel wool can simulate shadows. Roofing granules are another useful textural tool, and so is the net.

Nets garnished with painted or dyed fabrics do well for many concealment tasks. The net is an eminently useful tool— it is versatile in both color and texture. The effectiveness of netting depends on skillful texturing and achieving irregularity of the net's shadow. The net edges should always be terraced down to the ground to guard against the hard-outlined, hard-edged, straight-line shadow which provides that giveaway contrast. There are no straight lines or right angles in nature; shadows taking those forms are telltale and the net stringer must look out for them. The properly installed net should sag as little as possible.

Nets are garnished with strips of fabric; the effective garnishing density varies from one-fourth to three-fourths of the total net area. Average obscurement calls for one-third garnishing. In World War II the Army did this garnishing with five-foot lengths of Osnaburg fabric or burlap, cut two inches wide, hanging the fabric on fishnets in the field or on chicken wire at permanent locations. Phenolic enamel kept wire nets from rusting.

If you use nets you must take into consideration their snow and ice loads. Fresh-fallen snow weighs 8 pounds per cubic foot, ice 56 pounds per cubic foot. In this country load requirements are 40 pounds per square foot in Maine, New Hampshire, Vermont, northern New York, Wisconsin, Minnesota, Michigan, the Dakotas, Montana, and Wyoming. For other areas, requirements range down from 30 to 10 pounds per square foot.

SUMMING UP

All of the camouflage techniques are interdependent. The camouflage engineer has to worry about all of them in his work. In planning camouflage for a factory, for example, he must: (a) take fullest advantage of natural concealment; (b) make it compatible with the type of terrain; (c) use paint and netting to reduce the light reflection, break up the shadows, and modify the reflectivity of the building's structure; (d) disguise shapes and purposes (conceal smokestacks, for example).

When he's done all that, he's turned color to bear on one of its most important contributions to industry—defending the industry and the country from attack.

APPENDIX A

THE RIGHT COLOR NAMES

As color becomes more and more important in modern business and industry, the job of creating effective names for different colors becomes increasingly more complex and important. Today, in many instances, the right color name is just as important as the color itself in building acceptance for a product, store interior, or what-have-you.

But how do you create a good color name whenever you need one? What factors go into the choice of a new color name? What specialized research must you do in this field? How can you make sure you have the best possible color name for your product? All these are questions that must be answered in every business today—and answered correctly. To guide you in these answers, I have prepared from my own records, accumulated from many sources over the past twenty-five years, a comprehensive list of color names. Before we get to the list and its use, however, let's build some background about color names, as such.

Why Color Names Are Important

Here, the answer to the old question "What's in a name?" is "Plenty." Research tell us that good color names help increase sales, and that poor color names often detract from sales. Or think of it from another angle. Suppose your color name is right, that it conveys exactly the meaning it should. That indicates it has value of its own. And so has your product. So you get value plus value—which adds up to this: The right color name can usually create extra appeal and value for your product.

There are many other things good color names can contribute to a successful color program. The right descriptive color name helps prepare the customer for what he is going to get or see, and it carries conviction and extra meaning. In other words, it helps in the selling process. On another level, the right color name helps in business communication: the right descriptive name can help to tell people just what color you are talking about.

Studies have shown that good color names help in telephone and written communication, in preparing sales manuals, in presentations—and of course, in advertising and at the point of sale. Not only that, but the right name will suggest product qualities such as inherent value, durability, prestige, and fashion. When your name does all these things, you can be sure you've got a good one!

Here's an example of a good color name at work: In the automotive industry, it was once difficult to sell a maroon finish with a yellowish cast—even though the color was an excellent one for cars. In England, I noticed that automobiles built for King George VI by his coachmaker, Hooper & Company, were all finished in a maroon of this type. A sample of this color was obtained and an exact match of the English maroon was prepared for the American market. The American maroon was named King George Maroon—and from then on it received wide and continued acceptance. The right name had sold the finish.

252

Background on Color Names

Relatively few people, other than color engineers and scientists, need to describe or specify color with such precision as this:

White—the color of a freshly shaved piece of chalk observed at 10 A.M. on a clear day in June in Washington, D.C., against a lamp-black background.

But the language of color has suffered from a lack of systematic organization for many thousands of years.

Even such a master of description as Robert Louis Stevenson was at a loss to convey a satisfactory idea of a color he wanted. From the South Seas he wrote to a friend in London asking for a wallpaper with a background of a certain red, but after comparing the shade to others, he, at the end, confessed that he was quite unable to describe it. He wrote, "For a little workroom of my own at the back, I should like to see some patterns of unglossy—well I'll be hanged if I can describe this red—it's not Turkish and it's not Roman and it's not Indian, but it seems to partake of the last two and yet it can't be either of them because it ought to be able to go with vermilion."

Today, we still have the same problems in color nomenclature. E. N. Gathercoal, studying some of the colors of products listed in the *United States Pharmacopoeia,* found that the color names applied to the same object by several observers "may vary slightly in meaning, but there is frequently a wide variation in the actual color names employed to describe the same color." Six of the variations he found are indicated in a comparison table.

Every person interested in color should remember these stories. When you have the colors, name them. To help you do this, an extensive color-name list is included in Appendix A. It lists both alphabetically and by hue those names commonly used to describe color. Color identification can also be conveyed by modifiers, such as light, pale, bright, vivid, brilliant, deep, and dark.

COLOR NAMES APPLIED TO SIX SUBSTANCES

Substance	COLOR NAME APPLIED BY				
	Artist	Bacteriologist	Pharmacognosist	Pharmacist	Botanist
Paraffin Wax	White	White	Opaque White	White, Opaque	White
Panama Gum	Grayish Lemon	Grayish Yellow	Yellow Amber	Transparent Yellow	Yellow-Orange
Frankincense	Light Amber Yellow	Opaque Cream Yellow	Yellowish Brown	Opaque Light Reddish Brown	Light Reddish Buff
Succinum, Ambra Flava	Deep Cadmium	Medium Orange-Brown	Orange Amber	Yellow Amber	Reddish Brown
Cherry Gum	Dark Burnt Orange	Deep Brownish Red	Dark Reddish Brown	Reddish Amber, Opaque	Dark Orange Amber

Need for Color Names

Today's necessary profusion of colors calls for a profusion of color names, if only to give each manufacturer individuality

254

and selling opportunities. To unfamiliar eyes, the Arctic tundra appears to be gray-green, brown, or green-brown. It would be difficult for a stranger to name and distinguish between more than ten colors there. The Arctic native, however, has and needs five to eight hundred words and word combinations for the tundra's colors and their countless gradations. We have an equal need for names to deal with the color complexity of our own culture.

Lists of Color Names *

RED, PINK
DESCRIPTIVE NAMES

American	Coral	Hematite	Port Wine
Beauty	Coronation	Hollyhock	Raspberry
Apple	Cranberry	Indian	Redwood
Arbutus	Crimson	Lobster	Rose
Autumn	Currant	Lotus	Ruby
Azalea	Dragon's	Madeira	Salmon
Baby	Blood	Mandarin	Scarlet Lake
Barn	Dusty Pink	Marine	Sealing Wax
Begonia	Dusty Rose	Maroon	Shell
Bittersweet	Embers	Misty Rose	Shrimp
Blood	Fez	Mulberry	Strawberry
Blossom	Fire	Nasturtium	Sumac
Brick	Firecracker	Ocher	Sweet William
Bridal	Firefly	Old Rose	Taupe Rose
Bright	Flame	Onion	Tea Rose
Burgundy	Flesh	Pastel	Tile
Cardinal	Frosty	Peach	Titian
Carnation	Garnet	Peach Blossom	Tomato
Carrot	Geranium	Pepper	Tourmaline
Cherry	Grenadier	Pigeon Blood	Turkey
Claret	Grenadine	Pimento	Vandyke
Cloud	Harvard	Pink	Vermilion
Clover	Crimson	Pomegranate	Wine
Cochineal	Heather	Poppy	

* Some of the color names in this section are reproduced, with permission, from the International Correspondence School Instruction Text, *Color: Its Theory and Application* by Howard Ketcham.

RED, PINK
FASHION NAMES

Adrianople	Chalet	Egyptian	Insignia
After Glow	Charm	El Alamein	Inspiration
Ambassador	Chimney	Eureka	Liberty
Ambrosia	Cloud Rose	Eventide	Mandarin
Antwerp	Coca-Cola	Festoon	Mexican
Arabia	Colonial	Fiesta	Mignon
Artillery	Coquette	Fire	Morning Mist
Ashes of Roses	Corsage	Flare	Morocco
Blush	Damask	Geisha	Nude
Bonfire	Debutante	Grenadier	Nymph
Candy	Devil's	Gypsy	Winetone
Carnival	Dusk	Heavenly	Zest

ORANGE
DESCRIPTIVE NAMES

Apricot	Flamingo	Orange-Red	Pumpkin
Bright	Lacquer	Orange-Rust	Sun
Brilliant	Light	Orange-Yellow	Sunset
Bronze	Madder	Orpiment	Tangerine
Burnt	Marigold	Paprika	Terra Cotta
Copper	Nasturtium	Persian Melon	Tiger Lily
Dusty	Nassau	Persimmon	Yolk
Flame	Orange	Princeton	

FASHION NAMES

Capucine	Midnight Sun	Spanish	Suntan
Cuban	Mikado	Sunburst	Swamp Holly
Gold	Peruvian	Sun God	Tangier
Golden Girl	Punjab	Sun Kiss	Toboggan
Indian River	Seville	Sunkist	Vivacious
Killarney	Sierra	Sunstone	

BROWN, BEIGE, TAN
DESCRIPTIVE NAMES

Adobe	Bamboo	Buff	Cartridge
African	Beach	Burnt Rose	Cashew Nut
Almond	Beaver	Burnt Sienna	Cattail
Amber	Beige	Butterscotch	Cedar
Auburn	Bisque	Camel	Champagne
Autumn	Blond	Caramel	Chestnut

BROWN, BEIGE, TAN
DESCRIPTIVE NAMES

Chocolate	Luggage	Oatmeal	Sherry
Cinnamon	Macaroon	Otter	Snuff
Clove	Mahogany	Pecan	Sparrow
Cocoa	Manila	Putty	Spice
Coconut	Maple	Raffia	Sponge
Coffee	Maple Sugar	Roan	Sunburn
Copper	Martini	Rose	Taffy
Cordovan	Medal Bronze	Russet	Tanbark
Cork	Mince Meat	Russian Calf	Toast
Covert	Morocco Sand	Rust	Tobacco
Deep	Mushroom	Sable	Tortoise
Desert	Muskrat	Saddle	Turf
Desert Sand	Mustard	Sahara	Walnut
Ecru	Metallic	Sand	Warm Sepia
Fawn	Nubian	Sandstone	Wheat
Ginger	Nude	Sand Stucco	Winter Leaf
Golden	Nutmeg	Satinwood	Wood
Hazel	Oak	Seal	Woodbark
Honey	Oakwood	Sepia	

FASHION NAMES

Antique	Falcon	Nutmeg	Russian
Army	Florida Sand	Paddock	Samovar
Ascot	Gypsy	Padre	Sandalwood
Aztec	Hollywood	Pampas	Sea Sand
Bermuda	Hot Chocolate	Panama Sand	Seminole
Bone	Java	Pawnee	Solitaire
Brussels	Jungle	Pebble	Sorghum
Buckskin	Malacca	Peruvian	Stag
Butternut	Malibu	Polo	Stone
Casino	Meerschaum	Pongee	Sultan Sand
Catalina	Miami Sand	Pony	Tennis Court
Cimarron	Mode	Prout's	Town
Cuban Sand	Mohawk	Racquet	Tropical
Daytona	Mushroom	Rancho	Tuscany
Dessert	Nomad	Rosewood	Vienna
Driftwood	Navajo	Rum	Zuni

YELLOW, GOLD
DESCRIPTIVE NAMES

Amber	Daffodil	Honeydew	Saffron
Antique	Daisy	Jonquil	Squash
Apricot	Dust	Lemon	Straw
Blond	Forsythia	Maize	Sulphur
Butter	Gold	Melon	Sun
Buttercup	Gold Leaf	Mimosa	Sunflower
Butterscotch	Golden	Mineral	Sunlight
Canary	Golden	Mustard	Tulip
Chamois	Apricot	Nasturtium	Wheat
Cheddar	Grain	Old Gold	Wicker
Chrysanthemum	Grapefruit	Peanut	Zinnia
Citron	Hay	Pineapple	
Colonial	Hemp	Powdered	
Corn	Honey	Primrose	

FASHION NAMES

After Glow	Earth	Ingenue	Sombrero
Ambertone	Empire	Insignia	Southern Sun
Autumn	Fairy	Nugget	Spectrum
Beach	Gay	Pastel	Spring
Brimstone	Glint O'Gold	Pheasant	Sunlure
Burnt Brandy	Glow	Pirate	Sunrise
Celestial	Gold Rush	Pom Pom	Titian
Cheerful	Golden Gate	Poppy	Tropic Sand
Cigarette	Harvest	Radiant	Veiled Sun
Cloud	Imperial	Ray	Winter Sun
Cream	Inca	Shining	
Desert Dust	Indian	Siam Sand	
Dusty	Indian Wheat	Snow	

GREEN
DESCRIPTIVE NAMES

Almond	Citron	Fern	Hooker
Aqua	Cress	Fir	Hunter
Aquamarine	Cypress	Foliage	Ice
Asparagus	Dusty	Gage	Ivy
Billiard	Egyptian	Grass	Jade
Bottle	Emerald	Heather	Juniper
Bud	Evergreen	Highland	Kelly
Chicory	Fairway	Holly	Laurel

GREEN
DESCRIPTIVE NAMES

Leaf	Nile	Pine	Turquoise
Leek	Olive	Pistachio	Vibrant
Lettuce	Olive Drab	Sea	Viridian
Lime	Palm	Shamrock	Willow
Lizard	Palmetto	Slate	Woodland
Lush	Paris	Spectrum	Yew
Malachite	Parrot	Sprout	Yule Tree
Medium	Parsley	Spruce	Zircon
Ming	Patina	Surf	
Mint	Pea	Teal	
Misty	Pepper	Thyme	

FASHION NAMES

Arcadia	Gay	Paddock	Sulphate
Autumn Aqua	Garland	Phantom	Summer
Berkshire	Gumdrop	Pinebud	Tranquil
Bitter	Hillside	Pinemoss	Tropical
Burbank	Island	Porcelain	Turf
Christmas	Killarney	Primeval	Vagabond
Chrysolite	Mango	Primitive	Velvet
Erin	Marsh	Reseda	Verdant
Fern Leaf	Meadowbrook	Seacrest	Verde
Festive	Monaco	Seafoam	Victorian
Fluorite	Ocean Spray	Seaspray	
Frappé	Olivine	Seawater	

BLUE
DESCRIPTIVE NAMES

Aqua	Cloisonné	Dusty	Haze
Aquamarine	Cobalt	Turquoise	Holland
Antwerp	Colonial	Dutch	Horizon
Azure	Copenhagen	Electric	Huckleberry
Baby	Cornflower	Eton	Hyacinth
Baltic	Cyan	Federal	Indigo
Blue Bird	Dark Navy	Flag	Infantry
Blue Jay	Delft	Forget-me-not	Ink
Butterfly	Delphinium	French	Iris
Capri	Dragonfly	Gainsborough	King's
Cerulean	Dresden	Gobelin	Lake
Chalk	Dusty	Grape	Lake Como

BLUE

Lapis Lazuli	Navy	Princess	Teal
Larkspur	Opal	Robin's Egg	Turquoise
Limoges	Oriental	Sapphire	Twilight
Mallard	Oxide	Sea	Venetian
Marine	Pastel	Sèvres	Wedgwood
Middy	Peacock	Sky	Windsor
Midnight	Periwinkle	Slate	Wisteria
Milky	Persian	Spectrum	Yale
Mist	Porcelain	Steel	
Monastral	Powder	Storm	

FASHION NAMES

Academy	Dawn	Madonna	Sailor
Admiral	Dazzle	Magic Moon	Ship's
Annapolis	Debonair	Mediterranean	Sistine
Baltic	Diva	Middy	Spiritual
Bavarian	Dragon	Military	Squall
Bayou	Easter Bonnet	Monet	Starlight
Bimini	Enamel	Monterey	Static
Blueberry	Ensign	Mosaic	Stormy Night
Blue Devil	Ethereal	Mystic	Strato
Blue Flower	Faraway	National	Stratosphere
Blue Hour	Fidelity	Nattier	Southern
Blue Light	Florentine	Neapolitan	Sublime
Blue Ridge	Grotto	Newport	Triumph
Boatswain	Gulf	Norse	Trooper
Bonnie	Harbor	Northern Skies	Tropic
Brittany	Harlequin	Olympian	Tunis
Cascade	Harmony	Pagoda	Universal
Ceylon	Heaven	Palace	Vapor
Chantilly	Hussar	Peasant	Viking
China	Illusion	Phantom	Yacht
Classic	Imperial	Pilot	Zenith
Como	Italian	Pottery	
Continental	Jewel	Princely	

PURPLE

Amethyst	Aster	Eggplant	Grape
Amherst	Crocus	Fuschia	

PURPLE
DESCRIPTIVE NAMES

Imperial	Lavender	Mauve	Twilight
Chinese	Lilac	Orchid	Violet
Iris	Loganberry	Plum	
Lake	Madder	Raisin	
Larkspur	Magenta	Royal	

FASHION NAMES

Ash Mauve	Radiance	Serenade	Windflower
Dawn	Regal	Sorcerer	Winterwine
Imperial	Renaissance	Vino	
Parma	Romance	Viola	

BLACK
DESCRIPTIVE NAMES

Blackberry	Graphite	Loam	Shadow
Carbon	Ink	Midnight	Slate
Charcoal	Ivory	Night	Soot
Coal	Jet	Raven	Velvet
Ebony	Lamp	Sable	

FASHION NAMES

Despair	Midnight	Stygian

WHITE
DESCRIPTIVE NAMES

Alabaster	Ghost	Moth	Sheepskin
Beeswax	Glacier	Oxford	Sheet
Bone	Honeycomb	Paper	Snow
Cameo	Ivory	Parchment	Sodium
Chalk	Lily	Pearl	Star
Cloud	Magnesium	Platinum	Starch
Crystal	Milk	Polar	Stone
Fog	Mistletoe	Polar Bear	String
Frost	Moon	Popcorn	Tooth

FASHION NAMES

Bridal	Igloo	Oyster	Promise
Clair de lune	Moonglow	Pearly Gate	Starlight
Eskimo			

GRAY

Battleship	Gull	Pigeon	Smoke
Charcoal	Gun Metal	Pussy Willow	Squirrel
Cobweb	Lava	Quail	Stone
Elephant Skin	Lead	Quaker	Stratosphere
Engine	Mist	Rail	Traprock
Fog	Opal	Shadow	Zinc
French	Owl	Shark	
Goat	Oxford	Silver	
Greyhound	Pearl	Slate	

FASHION NAMES

Cadet	Dover	Modest	Sea Bird
Château	Gargoyle	Moon Mist	Storm
Dawn	Ghost	Old	Tint
Elephant's Breath	Lady	Puritan	
	London Fog	Sand Drift	

METALLIC

DESCRIPTIVE NAMES

Bronze	Gold	Platinum	Steel
Chrome	Lead	Silver	Tin
Copper			

FASHION NAMES

Bronze Glo	Coppertone

262

APPENDIX B

1. Blue, red
2. 13 through 15
3. Color
4. 10,000,000
5. Men
6. (a) Colors in which blue predominates
   (b) Colors in which red or yellow predominate
7. (a) Blue
   (b) Red
8. No. Primaries of pigment are red, yellow, and blue. Primaries of light are magenta, green, and violet-blue.
9. Black on yellow
10. (a) Using a light with a dark color
    (b) Using a color with its complement
    (c) Using a grayed color with a strong color, for example using olive green with emerald green
    (d) Using a warm color with a cold color
11. Yes
12. 50%

COLOR SYSTEMS

Which Is Best?

There is no point to arguing whether the Munsell or some other color system is best. Workable color systems provide an accurate color language. The choice of a system depends on its intended use. A *color appearance* or *color space* system is useful where color as *seen* is most important. Such a system can be used to file color samples, to record the colors of past production, or to describe a hypothetical color of which no samples are available.

A *color mixture* system helps most where color as *made* is important. It helps in calculating mixtures where samples already exist. Based on *additive mixture,* it prevents errors due to possible differences in pigments, dyes, or other colorants. And, of course, a color-mixture system is excellent where the materials are standardized and controlled.

The Tuning Fork of Colorimetry

We can identify a specific red as Munsell 6R 5/10, or a particular blue as Ostwald 13 ca, just as the musician can call a certain note middle C. But middle C has no meaning when our piano is out of tune. Science has helped the musician by defining middle C as a vibration of a definite wave length, and devising a tuning fork. How do we keep a color system in tune? How do we say which color is what, to begin with?

The science of Colorimetry helps us here. It analyzes physical color-data and treats it in ways which make the results apply to color, as we see and use it in practice. Instruments such as the recording spectrophotometer accurately measure color differences by reducing color to easily interpreted numerical values. Color data derived in this fashion never change.

Each color in the spectrum has a definite wave length. Reds, for example, extend from approximately 610 to about 700 millimicrons. Violets have wave lengths of approximately 400 to 450 millimicrons. Actual color samples, of course, do not reflect absolutely pure spectral light. Most reds, for example, would reflect small amounts of other wave lengths and a large amount of the wave lengths from 610 to 700 millimicrons. The reddest red hue is a dominant wave length located at a definite point.

Value can be measured by comparing the amount of light of all wave lengths reflected by a sample, with the amount of light reflected by a standard white (magnesium oxide is generally used). Light reflected from magnesium oxide remains constant and is, for all practical purposes, 100 per cent white. All other values are stated in percentages.

Under a white light, a given color reflects more light at and near its dominant wave length than from other parts of the visible spectrum. This gives rise to the sensation of hue.

The difference between the amount of light reflected at or near the dominant wave length and the average reflectance at other wave lengths gives rise to the attribute of chroma. The greater the difference the stronger the chroma.

For all scientific color measurements, a standard illuminant must be used, the most common being CIE * Standard Illuminant C, produced by a tungsten lamp with a prescribed filter and operated at a prescribed temperature.

We can now call cardinal red a color which, under Illuminant C, has a dominant wave length of 617 millimicrons (Munsell hue 5.5R), a reflectance of 9 per cent (Munsell value of /3.5), and a purity of 55 per cent (Munsell chroma of /9.5). Thus we have a *tuning fork* for the hue, value, and chroma of our color sample.

Some of the Applications

Color systems are used as a standard for teaching, understanding, measuring, and talking about color in precise terms. Once actual color samples have been developed and standardized, it is quicker to use *them* as working specifications, checking them occasionally with color system charts to be sure they have not altered or faded.

What would such a check show of some color standard we all know? Take the American flag, for example: The red in our flag in terms of Munsell attributes is approximately 5.5 red 4/14. And the blue is approximately 5 purple-blue 2/6.

The significance of color systems for determining color harmony is very slight. Perhaps a brief description of one of the best-known color systems would be of interest to the reader at this point.

The Munsell Color System †

The Munsell System is essentially a scientific concept for describing and analyzing color in terms of three attributes, identified in this system as hue, value and chroma. The method of color notation developed by A. H. Munsell, as the principal feature of this system, arranges the three attributes of color in orderly scales of equal visual steps, so that the attributes become dimensions or parameters by which color may be analyzed and described accurately under standard conditions of illumination.

* Commission Internationale de l'Éclairage.
† Reproduced by permission of Munsell Color Company.

266

Appendix C

Chromatic colors in the Munsell System of Color Notation are divided into five principal classes which are given the hue names of red, yellow, green, blue, and purple. A further division yields the five intermediate hue names of yellow-red, green-yellow, blue-green, purple-blue, and red-purple, these being combinations of the five principal hues. Hence the hue notation of any color indicates its relation to the five principal and intermediate hues or any of their subdivisions. Capitalized initials such as "R" for red, or "YR" for yellow-red, are used as symbols for the hue names. When finer subdivisions are needed, the ten hue names or symbols may again be combined to produce such combinations as red-yellow-red, which is symbolized "R-YR." For even finer divisions, the hues may be divided into ten steps each (1R to 10R and 1YR to 10YR), thus increasing the hue notation to 100.

The value notation indicates the degree of lightness or darkness of a color in relation to a neutral gray scale, which extends from a theoretically pure black symbolized as 0/ to a theoretically pure white symbolized as 10/. A gray or a chromatic color that appears visually halfway in lightness between pure black and pure white has a value notation of 5/. Lighter colors are indicated by numbers ranging above five, while darker ones are indicated by numbers below five.

The chroma notation of a color indicates the strength (saturation) or degree of departure of a particular hue from a neutral gray of the same value. The scales of chroma extend from /0 for a neutral gray out to /10, /12, /14, or farther, depending upon the strength or saturation of the individual color. A color classified popularly as "vermilion" might have a chroma as strong as /12, while another color of the same hue and value classified popularly as "rose" might have a chroma as weak as /4.

Whenever a finer division is needed for any of the three attributes, decimals may be used, such as 2.5R 4.5/2.4.

The complete Munsell notation for any chromatic color is written hue value/chroma, or symbolically H V/C. A particular sample of vermilion might then have a Munsell notation of 5R 5/12, while a particular sample of rose might have a notation of 5R 5/4.

The notation for a neutral gray is written N V/C. A very dark neutral (black) would be written N 1/0, and N 9/0 would be the notation for a very light neutral (white). For grays of slight chromaticity, the notation is written N V/(H,C), using only the symbols for the ten major hues to indicate the hue; thus a gray of a slightly yellowish appearance is written N 8/(Y 0.4).

267

The Munsell System of Color Notation can be thought of in terms of a color solid or color space in which the value scale runs vertically from a theoretically pure black at the bottom to a theoretically pure white at the top, while the various hues are located around it, describing an approximately cylindrical shape with the neutral value scale in its center. The chroma scales radiate from the vertical value scale in the center to the periphery of the color solid in equal visual steps. The typical hue circle shows five principal and five intermediate hues located around its circumference.

Because of the accurate notation of observed color made possible by the Munsell System, science and industry have an excellent tool for evaluating various products and certain phenomena in terms of color. Specifications for paint, ink, hay, cotton, tomatoes, and many other products include Munsell notations as the standard reference for grading colors. The bacterial content of raw milk, as well as different types of soil and rocks may be quickly and efficiently studied by referring to a color standard bearing a Munsell notation. Furthermore, reference to a standard with a Munsell notation eliminates the confusion about color which is often caused by geography; 5R 5/12 is precisely the same color in India as it is in Los Angeles, when viewed under standard conditions of illumination.

The arts also benefit by the Munsell System of Color Notation. An artist who is sufficiently familiar with the system may record the color notation of a particular scene or object on a rough sketch and reproduce those colors accurately at his leisure. Reflectance is an important consideration in both architecture and interior decoration, and a chart photometer which measures reflectance quickly and accurately for three standard illuminants has been developed using colors with Munsell notations. The Munsell color solid is an excellent study in color relationships, and for teaching this color system, charts and other educational tools are available.

The Munsell System of Color Notation has made possible the practical application of color to many problems, but there is ample scope for this system in many areas where the possibilities for evaluation, analysis, and control through the use of color have not been fully realized. Research on any problem in which color is an important factor will depend upon accurate color standards.

Color Systems Are Not the Complete Answer

There is nothing wrong with the principles upon which any good color system is based. There is everything wrong with *any* system for finding correct color combinations in the absence of a good basic color sense in the user. The best creative color work cannot be oversimplified. Usually color systems feature a series of color charts divided into a number of basic color families or hues. This is excellent as far as it goes. But since there are thousands of variations of hue, value and chroma for each of these basic color families and no guidance for selection among them, these charts are of limited practical value in working out distinctive and unusual color relationships.

The only practical color harmony guides worth their salt in industry are the ones worked out by skilled professionals specializing in the use of color. These suggest *specific* combinations, based on actual product color representations. As a result all of the ensembles suggested are likely to be in good taste and not commonplace or obvious.

There is a decided trend these days on the part of manufacturers to present their floor tiles, paints, plastics, inks, papers, etc. in this fashion as a customer service to build sales, profits, and good will.

Index

Index